Table Saws
& Techniques

Handyman Club Library™
Handyman Club of America
Minneapolis, Minnesota

Table Saws & Techniques

By Chris Marshall

CREDITS

Mike Vail
Vice President, New Product & Business Development

Tom Carpenter
Director of Books & New Media Development

Chris Marshall
Author and Editorial Coordinator

Mark Johanson
Book Products Development Manager

Dan Cary
Photo Production Coordinator

Steve Anderson
Senior Book Production Assistant

Bill Nelson
Series Design, Art Direction and Production

Mark Macemon
Lead Photographer

Ralph Karlen
Photography

Craig Claeys
Illustrator

John Drigot
Technical Illustrator

Eric Melzer
John Nadeau
Production Assistance

Dan Kennedy
Book Production Manager

Renier Antiques
Historical Table Saw Consultation and Imagery

PHOTO CREDITS
Pages 16, 17, 132, 140, 142
Delta International Machinery Corp.

Page 19
Laguna Tools

Page 130, 140
HTC Products, Inc.

Page 133
Incra Precision Tools

CONTRIBUTING MANUFACTURERS
Craftsman Tools
Delta International Machinery Corp.
HTC Products, Inc.

SPECIAL THANKS
Renata Mastrofrancesco, Delta International Machinery Corp.
Kelly Mehler, technical consultation
Paul Williams, Tried & True Tools, Fridley, MN

ISBN 1-58159-041-5

Handyman Club of America
12301 Whitewater Drive
Minnetonka, Minnesota 55343

Table Saws & Techniques

Table of Contents

Introduction

Buying your first table saw is a rite of passage for most handymen. There comes a point in your woodworking pursuits when you reach the cutting limits of your circular saw or jig saw and you want more: More versatility; more accuracy; more control; more power. A table saw will satisfy these needs and open new doors of possibility as your woodworking skills grow. You may discover that owning a table saw is just the push you've needed to step up to the challenges of more serious woodworking.

If you're a seasoned woodworker already, your table saw is no doubt a reliable companion in the shop. It is certainly one of a handful of tools that gets put through its paces on a regular basis and makes more sawdust than gathers dust. As you've surely discovered, once you've owned a table saw and put it to good use as a cutting, joint-making and shaping tool, it's hard to imagine doing without one.

Whether you've just unpacked your first table saw or have been using one for years, this book belongs in your shop. *Table Saws & Techniques,* created exclusively for members of the Handyman Club of America, was developed by table saw users for table saw users. We hope that you'll keep it next to your saw owner's manual as an essential source of no-nonsense information about using, maintaining and improving your saw. Our goal in creating this handbook is simple: We want you to maximize your saw's full potential in the safest way possible.

In this book, you'll learn the nuts and bolts of what makes a table saw the efficient cutting machine it is designed to be. We'll help you clarify the kinds of questions you should ask when making a decision about which saw to buy, even if it means purchasing a used saw instead of new. Should you decide to buy a used saw, this book outlines what you need to know to conduct a thorough saw inspection. If the saw passes these tests, you should go home with a sound saw that will give you years of good service.

Maybe your saw isn't cutting as accurately as it once did and is overdue for a thorough tune-up. We've dedicated a full chapter to tuning and maintenance, which walks you step-by-step through those essential tweaks and adjustments you should make from time to time to keep your saw in tip-top shape. If a good tune-up doesn't do the trick, you might be able to replace a part or two on your saw to boost its cutting performance. Read the chapter on sawing accessories to learn more about aftermarket safety and precision cutting devices that may be available for your saw. Customizing the tool you already own could save you hundreds of dollars over investing in a new saw.

But all of this information is secondary to what's most important to any woodworker: cutting wood. Using a table saw implies two requirements: First, saw with a working blade guard and splitter installed whenever the cut allows. (NOTE: *On some of the photographs in this book, the blade gusrd and splitter have been removed for photographic purposes only.*) Second, learn the fundamentals of safe sawing techniques. The largest section of this book will teach you what you need to know to saw safely. You'll learn about choosing and preparing lumber for the saw, selecting the proper blades for your cutting tasks, setting up your saw and your shop for safe sawing, and mastering essential table saw cuts, including ripping, crosscutting, mitering and more. We've included a complete chapter on essential table saw jigs you can build to make your saw even more versatile, as well as an exhaustive section on cutting a host of different joints to suit any project.

Finally, if you are a history buff, you'll appreciate studying a variety of different vintage table saws dotted throughout this book in sidebars on table saw history. The engravings and lithographs come from numerous tool catalogs printed over the last century and reveal a rich evolution of table saw style and improvements that have influenced the form and function of the saws we use today.

With more than 300 full-color photographs and illustrations, we hope this book will be a resource you'll pick up again and again to answer table saw questions, improve your sawing skills and help make your saw both accurate and a pleasure to use.

Table Saw Basics

Regardless of size, price or style, every table saw is really just a flat table through which a blade protrudes to cut lumber. A couple of fences—one running parallel to and another perpendicular to the blade—guide workpieces as you push them into the blade. Over the past century, table saws have taken various shapes and sizes, but they have always shared an efficient and time-tested relationship between table, fences and blade.

These days, table saws fit into three distinct families that span considerable ranges in price, features and performance: benchtop saws, contractor's saws and cabinet saws. This chapter will help you understand those anatomical features shared by all saws, then clarify the differences between each saw family.

If you are preparing to buy your first table saw, use these pages to familiarize yourself with the kinds of questions you should ask before you buy. Then, try out a few saws to see which features and level of performance suit your needs. Ask questions of tool dealers. Read saw reviews published in reputable woodworking magazines, especially annual tool buyers' guides where saws are ranked side by side. Attend woodworking shows that come to your town and watch table saw demonstrations. Be curious and diligent, and you'll surely find a saw that fits your woodworking or workshop needs perfectly.

On the other hand, if you are already on your second or third table saw, take a few moments to skim this chapter as a good refresher on the basics. It never hurts to reaffirm what you already know.

Finally, study the safety issues outlined at the end of this chapter to learn more about how you can outfit yourself, and your saw, for safe, pleasurable sawing.

Anatomy of a table saw

Throatplate

Blade guard

Miter gauge

Splitter with antikickback pawls

Blade

Rip fence

Fence rail

Miter slot

Extension wing

Table

Fence rail

Motor

ON/OFF switch

Fence locking lever

Blade tilt scale

Saw base

Blade-elevating handwheel

CRAFTSMAN
CONTRACTOR SERIES
10" Belt Drive   3 HP

Saw table styles

Cabinet saws: **Both the center table and extension wings on cabinet saws are made of cast iron, the most durable and flat tabletop material available. All of this iron adds a considerable amount of stability–and weight–to the saw.**

Contractor's saws: **The center section of the saw table is cast iron, but the extension wings often are made of pressed steel or webbed cast iron (as shown here) instead of solid cast iron. Cast-iron extension wings are preferred over pressed steel.**

Benchtop saws: **The saw table and extension wings on most benchtop saws are made of a single piece of cast aluminum, which is lighter and generally less flat than iron tabletops.**

Table saw anatomy

Here is a brief overview of the major components found on most table saws.

Saw table

The center section of most *saw tables* is made of cast iron to provide a rugged and dead-flat surface. Some saw manufacturers use aluminum alloys for saw tables to cut down on weight, particularly on portable benchtop saws. Saw tables may either be one piece or a combination of a center cast table with two *extension wings* bolted on each side. Extension wings are made of cast iron or pressed steel, and they enlarge the overall tabletop to support larger workpieces.

Throatplate

Saw tables are equipped with a removable insert, called a *throatplate,* that surrounds the saw blade and sits flush with the tabletop in a recessed opening. Essentially, throatplates serve two functions: they support workpieces at the point of contact with the blade, and they provide quick access to the blade arbor for maintenance and blade changes.

Most throatplates do not fasten into the throatplate opening in the table, although some have a metal "nub" that catches underneath the saw table to keep the throatplate from lifting up during a cut. Throatplates typically employ two to four allen screws so the plate can be adjusted flush with the table surface. Aftermarket throatplates are available for use with dado blades or molding heads. You can also build your own throatplates from hardwood (See page 33).

Throatplates **that come with most table saws (A) are made of soft cast metal. You can also buy metal dado-blade throatplates (B) and plastic "zero-clearance" throatplate blanks (C). A throatplate does not have to be made of either metal or plastic; hardwood (D) is a suitable alternative and just as safe.**

Rip fence styles

Button

Two-rail fences, the most common fence style, clamp to tubular rails on the front and back of the saw table. A rod extends through the fence body and attaches to a hook-shaped clamp (See inset photo) on the back end of the fence. When you lock down the fence in front, the rod pulls the hook tight in back.

T-square fences, a newer and generally more accurate fence design, clamp to a single hollow rail along the front edge of the saw table. The back of the fence simply rests on a metal bar. Some T-square fences use an adjustable metal button (See inset photo) to glide on the back bar.

Miter slots & rip fence

You must pass workpieces straight through the blade to cut them accurately. Any deviation from a straight path will lead to sloppy cuts, unsafe sawing conditions or both. Saw tables are outfitted with an adjustable *rip fence* and *miter gauge* to make guiding workpieces easy and safe. Two parallel *miter slots* machined across the saw table on each side of the blade serve as tracks for the miter gauge.

Rip fences guide boards so they remain parallel to the blade when they are cut lengthwise (called *rip-cutting*). Depending on the saw, the rip fence body will be made of steel or extruded aluminum and possibly faced with plastic or laminated wood to provide a slippery, smooth bearing surface for guiding workpieces.

Rip fences must be adjustable so workpieces can be rip-cut to different widths. Typically, rip fences slide on one or two *fence rails* mounted along the front and back edges of the saw table (See top photos). Some rails are made of steel or extruded aluminum tubing, while others are simply lengths of "L"-shaped steel bar. Lower-priced saws may even have fence rails that are molded into the saw table (See bottom photo, right).

The front fence rail is equipped with a measurement scale to help index the rip fence a specific distance from the blade. A lever and clamp mounted on the front of the rip fence pulls the fence tight against the saw table and locks it in place.

Guard & splitter

Every table saw comes outfitted with a plastic or metal *blade guard,* which shrouds the blade, protecting you from exposure to the blade teeth as well as sawdust and wood chips that are blown upward by the

Most benchtop saws have crude, light-duty fences that clamp directly to the saw table. A flat plate on the end of the fence (See inset photo) helps to pull the fence tight.

blade. On most saws, a metal plate called a *splitter* anchors the guard and aligns it with the blade. The primary purpose of a splitter is to keep wood from pinching the back (outfeed) side of the blade during rip cuts. Splitters are outfitted with a pair of spring-loaded *antikickback pawls* that allow a workpiece to slide in only one direction—from the infeed side to the outfeed side of the blade. In the event that the blade should grab a board and attempt to shoot it back out of the cut (a dangerous condition called kickback), the sharp points on the pawls grab the wood and hold it against the saw table.

Every table saw needs a functional guard and splitter to operate safely. But splitters tend to fall out of alignment and guards can obscure your line of sight

The guard, splitter and antikickback pawls **protect you from exposure to the blade as well as workpiece kickback. Standard blade guards attach with a pivoting arm to the splitter, so the guard can ride up and over a workpiece, then drop back into place against the saw table.**

Miter gauges, **used for making crosscuts and miter cuts, have a swiveling protractor-style head mounted on a bar that fits into the miter slots in the saw table. A handle screws into the bar and locks the fence.**

when you make cuts, so many saw owners remove the guard assembly and set it aside permanently. CAUTION: *Regardless of how much easier it may be to saw without a blade guard and splitter in place, you are completely vulnerable to both cuts and kickback without these safety items. Leave them on your saw for every cut that allows them, or replace them with an aftermarket guard and splitter (See pages 134 to 136).*

Miter gauge

A miter gauge is comprised of a swiveling metal head mounted on a flat metal bar that tracks in the miter slots. The front of the head is flattened into a short fence. A miter gauge is used for making crosscuts on either side of the blade. The head functions like a protractor, so it can be set and locked to any angle between 30° and 90°. Most miter gauges are outfitted with adjustable positive stops at 90° and 45°.

When the miter gauge head is set at 90°, the miter slots ensure that a workpiece held against the miter gauge will meet the blade squarely (called *crosscutting*).

Saw controls

Most table saws are outfitted with two *handwheels* that are used to adjust the blade. The front handwheel allows you to raise and lower the blade, and the side handwheel controls blade tilt. Worm gears on the ends of the handwheel shafts mesh with teeth on either the front trunnion or the arbor assembly and pivot these parts (See *Illustration,* next page). A few models incorporate both blade tilt and blade height functions into one handwheel. On these saws, the handwheel is switched between tilting and height adjustments by flipping a lever located behind or near the handwheel. In either case, once you've set the blade, you simply tighten a knob in the center hub of each handwheel to lock in the blade settings.

The *ON/OFF switch* on any saw should be positioned prominently and within easy reach. You should be able to trigger the ON/OFF switch without looking at it. Move the switch box on the saw base if it's in an inconvenient place so you can shut the saw off instinctively and quickly in the event of an emergency.

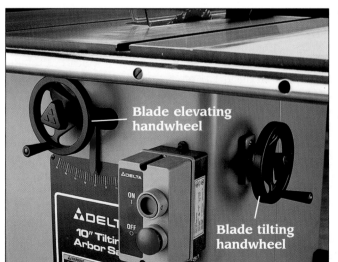

Table saw operating controls **should be accessible and sturdy. This cabinet saw features large ON/OFF buttons, an easy-to-read blade tilt scale and rugged steel handwheels located within easy reach from the front of the saw.**

Interior table saw components

The layout and shape of individual saw parts will vary from saw to saw, especially on benchtop models, but here are the essential mechanicals contained in most saws:

A. Blade-tilting handwheel
B. Blade-elevating handwheel
C. Blade-tilting worm gears
D. Front trunnion
E. Throatplate

F. Arbor assembly
G. Blade arbor
H. Rear trunnion
I. Motor
J. Rear cradle

K. Motor pulley
L. Drive belt
M. Arbor pulley
N. Blade-elevating worm gears
O. Front cradle

Motor & inner mechanicals

Table saw "transmissions" consist of an electric *motor*, which sits beneath the saw table or hangs behind it to drive the blade. The blade mounts with a large nut to a shaft called an *arbor*, which spins on two or more sealed bearings set into a cast-iron or steel *arbor assembly*. (In the case of benchtop table saws, which will be discussed later in this chapter, the blade may bolt directly to the motor shaft, so the motor shaft serves as the arbor.) The motor transfers power to the blade by way of one to three V-shaped flexible *drive belts* and a couple of *pulleys* mounted on the motor and arbor shafts.

The arbor assembly connects to a cast-iron *cradle* that hangs from semicircular *trunnions* in front and back. The cradle holds the arbor assembly and motor in line with one another so the drive belts do not have to twist as the arbor tilts. As you turn the *blade-tilting handwheel,* the cradle meshes with *worm gears* on the handwheel and slides along arcs formed on the trun-nions, which tilts the blade. When you turn the *blade-elevating handwheel* to raise and lower the blade, worm gears pivot the arbor up and down.

Refer to the illustration above for a general overview of saw mechanicals. The appearance of parts on your saw will vary. To acquaint yourself with the specific mechanicals of your saw, refer to the technical drawings printed in your owner's manual.

Saw base

All of a table saw's hardware and controls are contained in a sturdy *saw base*. Saw bases vary in construction, shape and size, but they provide a stable platform for the saw table, rip fence and mechanicals. Bases are made of either steel or high-impact plastic. Some bases form floor-standing cabinets (from which cabinet saws get their name), while other bases are shorter in order to sit on a worksurface or are outfitted with legs to make the saw floor-standing.

Benchtop saws

Benchtop table saws are the smallest table saws you can buy. Most saws in this category have tables that are less than 3 ft. wide and 2 ft. deep, so they can be transported easily. Weighing less than 50 pounds fully assembled, benchtop saws are easy for most people to carry by themselves.

Given their size and weight, benchtop saws are popular these days with contractors, who can tote them from job site to job site and set them up on the tailgate of a truck or on a couple of saw-horses. A benchtop saw may be a good choice for you if you are an occasional woodworker or week-end remodeler. Those who work in cramped basement shops or who need their full-time garage to double as a workshop will also appreciate the smaller proportions of a benchtop saw. Set it on a shelf or under a workbench, and it's out of the way, without sacrificing any additional floor space.

In addition to being fully portable, consumer-grade bench-

Benchtop saws are portable, powerful and inexpensive. Their lightweight construction, however, means they have smaller tabletops, often crude rip fences and miter gauges and make more noise. They can also produce more vibration than heavier saws. Benchtop saws are best suited for simple woodworking and remodeling tasks.

top saws are also the least expensive new saws to purchase. All benchtop saws run on standard 115-volt household current. Most benchtop models accept standard 10-in.-dia. table saw blades, so the small size of the saw doesn't limit your cutting capacity. Benchtop saws can also accept smaller diameter circular saw blades, as can most other table saws with 5/8-in. arbors.

Along with their advantages, benchtop saws have their limitations. Generally, benchtop saws have relatively crude rip fences that

A benchtop saw without a floor stand can tuck conveniently beneath a workbench or on a shelf, without taking up additional floor space in the shop. Weighing 50 pounds or less, these saws are easy for most people to lift and carry alone.

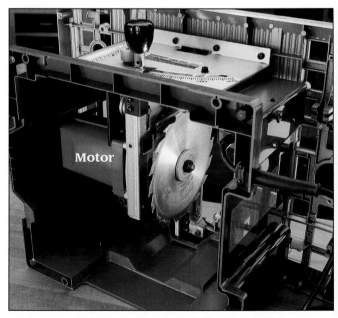

Blades mount directly to the motor shaft on a benchtop saw, just as they do on a portable circular saw. Raising, lowering and tilting the blade involves moving the motor as well as the blade. There are no drive belts to replace on direct-drive saws.

are difficult to keep adjusted, steel (rather than cast-iron) components in the undercarriage, and small miter gauges with less precise protractor scales. Saw tables are usually made of aluminum alloys rather than cast iron, so they aren't as rigid or flat as the tables on larger saws. Fortunately, the popularity of these saws is improving the quality of the components that manufacturers use, especially concerning rip fences. Some new benchtop saws are outfitted with rugged rip fences that use rack-and-pinion gears to make them capable of greater precision. But not all benchtop saws are created equally; price is a good indicator of quality.

Benchtop saws are *direct-drive* saws, which means the saw blade mounts directly to the motor shaft. There is no separate arbor shaft. These saws are powered by universal motors, the same motors used in hand-held power tools like routers, sanders, circular saws and corded drills. Universal motors are designed to develop peak power for short periods of time at high revolutions, so they run at relatively high amperage (usually around 15 amps). This means that benchtop saw motors are capable of short bursts of power, which may exceed even 2 h.p., but they can't sustain heavy sawing loads for cutting hardwoods, wet lumber or long, thick boards.

Larger contractor's and cabinet saws, as you'll see on the following pages, use slower-spinning induction motors that run at lower amperage (230-volt induction motors run at half the amperage of the average benchtop saw). Induction motors run cooler and maintain more even horsepower under load. Benchtop saws are

The layout of blade adjustment controls **will vary from saw to saw. This particular benchtop saw uses a knob rather than a handwheel to set blade height. A lever behind the knob controls blade tilt. This saw has scales for both blade height and tilt.**

powered by universal motors primarily because the motors are much lighter in weight and smaller proportionally than induction motors, so they fit into smaller, more confined saw bases. Universal motors are a perfectly suitable powerplant for occasional hard use. However, be aware that these motors are noisier, generate greater vibration and tend to wear out sooner than induction motors.

One drawback to benchtop saws **is that most are outfitted with lower-quality miter gauges and rip fences that are difficult to set precisely. On the benchtop saw miter gauge shown here, the protractor scale is calibrated in 5° increments, versus single-degree markings on the contractor's saw miter gauge. You'll need single-degree precision from a miter gauge if you plan to do complex woodworking.**

Benchtop saw miter gauge

Contractor's saw miter gauge

Contractor's saws

Contractor's saws **offer the best compromise between cost, quality and features in a full-sized table saw. Better-quality contractor's saws have cast-iron arbor and cradle assemblies as well as cast-iron saw tables and extension wings. Precision T-square fences and extension tables now come standard on many models.**

If you think about table saws as if they were cars, benchtop saws would be the subcompacts, while contractor's saws would be the mid-priced family sedans. This is because contractor's saws offer the best compromise between cost, quality and features in a full-sized table saw. Like their benchtop cousins, contractor's saws are designed to be somewhat portable, weighing between 200 and 300 pounds. But with an overall height of around 34 in., you wouldn't want to load and unload these saws from a vehicle on a daily basis. Any contractor's saw can be outfitted with a rolling saw base, however (See page 142), so the saw can be rolled wherever it is needed or out of the way for storage.

Contractor's saws are designed for rigorous daily use, whether you are a serious woodworking hobbyist, contractor or furniture builder. Typical saw table dimensions are around 40 in. wide and 27 in. deep, including extension wings, which gives most contractor's saws a *ripping capacity* (the distance from the blade to the furthest position of the rip fence away from the blade) of nearly 2½ ft. This table geometry makes contractor's saws capable of ripping full-sized sheets of plywood in half, lengthwise—an unwieldy feat on smaller saws.

One distinctive feature of a contractor's saw is the location of the motor, which hangs outside the saw base in back of the saw. The motor is mounted on a hinged plate, so the weight of the motor actually provides all the tension on the drive belt that spins the blade arbor.

Most contractor's saws are powered by a 1½- to 2-h.p. induction motor, a beefier power plant than a comparable universal motor. Outfitted with a 10-in.-dia. blade, a contractor's saw can cut through virtually any hardwood or softwood up to 3 in. thick in one pass. Many saws can be rewired to operate on either 115- or 230-volt current. Converting the motor from one voltage to the other isn't difficult; it's a simple matter of replacing the plug and power cord and reconnecting a few wires (See page 143).

Contractor's saws are pricier than benchtop saws, but the difference in price is easy to justify when you evaluate performance and features. Undercarriage components like the arbor and cradle assemblies typically are made of cast-iron, which means con-

Motor

Drive belt & belt cover

You can immediately identify a contractor's saw **if the motor hangs behind the saw base. A drive belt connects a pulley on the motor with a pulley on the blade arbor. Having the motor exposed makes it easier to maintain, but it enlarges the saw's overall footprint.**

The combination of price and performance make contractor's saws a lower-cost alternative to cabinet saws for professional woodworkers. This contractor's saw, located in a custom furniture shop, is outfitted with large extension and outfeed tables as well as a precision rip fence. The setup makes it easy for one builder to manage full-sized sheets of plywood.

tractor's saws deliver smoother cuts with minimal vibration. Plus, heavier cast-iron undercarriage parts will tend to keep a saw in tune longer than lighter-weight undercarriage parts.

One big advantage to contractor's saws is that they are the target tool for manufacturers of aftermarket add-on equipment. Manufacturers offer a wide assortment of precision rip fence systems, better quality miter gauges, improved blade guard systems and accessory sawing attachments like dado blades and molding head cutters. Some contractor's saws come with micro-adjustable rip fences and extension tables as standard items. These accessories can increase the ripping capacity of the saw from 2 ft. to more than 4 ft.

Aside from a higher price tag than most benchtop models, the downsides to owning a contractor's saw are few. But you should consider that contractor's saws unavoidably take up more floor space. Even without long extension tables, a basic contractor's saw will take up about the same amount of floor space as a small riding lawn tractor. Another nuisance involves dust collection. Both the bottom and back of the saw must be covered up to keep sawdust from blowing out of the saw or dropping to the floor. Some saws can be outfitted with a plate that covers the bottom of the saw base and a port for connecting to a shop dust-collection system (See page 141).

Table Saw History

Hand-powered sawing

Parks Self-Feed Rip Saw (circa 1892)

Prior to the mid 1920s, a saw was either belt-driven from a central power source in the factory or was hand- or foot-powered. Notice the large cast-iron flywheel and handle on the left side of this rip saw. An operator would spin the flywheel, and the weight of the wheel would keep the saw blade spinning while making a cut.

Cabinet saws

To continue the car analogy, cabinet saws are the luxury sedans of table saws. They are designed for professional use in commercial cabinet and woodworking shops, but are also widely available to woodworkers. What sets these saws apart from other table saws in terms of performance and reliability has to do mostly with sheer mass. Cabinet saws feature hefty cast-iron undercarriages and arbor assemblies. Saw tables are made of thicker cast iron, and most cabinet saws also have solid cast-iron extension wings, as opposed to pressed steel or webbed-iron extension wings found on other saws. To support all of this weight, cabinet saw bases are made of heavier-gauge steel and enclose the motor and arbor assembly on all four sides. Weighing in at more than 400 pounds, cabinet saws aren't portable, though they can be outfitted with rolling bases.

There are two advantages to all of this heavy metal: First, heavier components, particularly the arbor and cradle assemblies and motor mount, dampen vibration. The smoother the saw runs, the less vibrations gets transferred to the blade, resulting in smoother cuts. Smoother operation also means that cabinet saws stay in tune for longer periods of time than other saws, especially if they aren't moved around the shop.

The second advantage to heavier components is strength. To meet the demands of commercial woodworking, where they may be cutting thick hardwood or plowing dadoes all day long, most cabinet saws have heavy-duty 3- to 5-h.p. induction motors that run at 230 volts. The typical blade capacity is 10 in., but saws taking 12- and 14-in.-dia. blades are also available for commercial use.

Cabinet saws set the standard for reliability, accuracy and power in a table saw. Motor sizes range anywhere from 2 to 5 h.p. Saws with a 10-in.-dia. blade capacity are most common, but some manufacturers offer 12- and even 14-in.-dia. models.

Cast-iron cradle assembly

Motor

Cabinet saw motors mount to the underside of the saw table inside the cabinet. This helps reduce both noise and dust. Massive cast-iron cradle assemblies provide rock-solid transmission of power between the motor and the blade arbor. The bulk also helps soak up vibration.

To manage the torque that a larger motor develops, as well as to handle heavy stresses put on the saw blade, cabinet saws often use two or three drive belts to spin the arbor, as opposed to only one drive belt on contractor's saws. Brawny arbor and cradle parts ensure that the motor and belts won't twist the arbor assembly out of alignment. This way, the saw delivers power efficiently from motor to blade without compromising accuracy.

For all this performance and durability, the typical cabinet saw doesn't take up the floor space of a luxury car. Saw table dimensions are about the same as a contractor's saw, not including add-on accessories. Cabinet saws also handle dust collection more efficiently than benchtop or contractor's saws, mainly because the enclosed base captures the dust. Most cabinet saws come with a hose port built into the saw base, which can connect directly to a shop dust collection system.

A sizable range of aftermarket accessories are available for cabinet saws, such as precision rip fence and miter gauge systems, improved blade guards and splitters, outfeed support tables and rolling saw bases. For a sampling of these aftermarket accessories, see pages 130 to 143.

If all of this performance sounds appealing, brace yourself when you go shopping for a cabinet saw. Heavy-duty construction and professional-quality components don't come cheaply. Better-quality cabinet saws start at around two to three times the price of a contractor's saw, and you can spend as much as a good used car if you buy a professional-grade cabinet saw with all the accessories. Also be aware that you'll need 230-volt service in your shop to power up nearly any cabinet saw, which will probably require hiring an electrician on top of the cost of the saw.

Blade arbors on larger cabinet saws are usually made of cast iron, often outfitted with two to four drive pulleys and just as many drive belts. Notice the heft of the cast-iron arbor assembly and trunnions on this saw.

Rugged construction combined with a heavy-duty induction motor make cabinet saws the right choice for rigorous cutting tasks, like working with dense hardwoods or quantities of oversized lumber.

Which saw is right for you?

Despite the fact that there are only three basic saw types to choose from, picking the right saw can still be a tough decision. While the caliber of a saw you use will affect the quality of the cuts you make, spending more money on a professional-grade saw won't necessarily turn you into a better woodworker. Patience, experience and careful planning always influence how your projects turn out. On the other hand, buying a budget-priced saw that fits your needs today may leave you wanting more from your saw a year or two down the road. So choose a saw wisely, based on your skill level, woodworking expectations and budget. Here are a few issues to keep in mind when selecting a saw:

Evaluate your current sawing needs.

Consider the kind of woodworking you actually do today to clarify your present sawing needs. Someone who spends an occasional weekend in the shop building small, simple projects is obviously going to have different cutting needs than the person who builds cabinets or custom furniture for a living. If the sum total of your sawing amounts to making butt joints and simple bevel cuts with a circular saw, or if your "woodworking" really boils down to cutting framing lumber for remodeling projects, do you really need a saw with 30 in. of ripping capacity and a 3-h.p. motor? Probably not. A benchtop saw may be the practical solution for the kind of work you do.

If you spend the majority of your shop time remodeling **or building simple woodworking projects, a benchtop saw can provide you the versatility you need at an affordable price.**

Plan ahead.

In addition to evaluating your present needs, be forward-thinking about where your woodworking is headed in the future. If you see your woodworking interests growing, buy a saw that will continue to be a strong performer for years to come. For example, if shop space is at a premium, but you know you'll be cutting dadoes, thick lumber or larger sheet goods, think twice before you buy a benchtop table saw. Even though the size of the saw might fit perfectly in your present shop space, most benchtop saws are somewhat restrictive in terms of the quality and type of cuts they make. Plus, your accessory options will be limited (See *Chart,* page 131).

A better solution would be to rearrange your shop (and maybe toss some clutter) to make room for a larger contractor's saw. Think of it this way: When the size of your shop and your skill level grows—and both probably will—the saw will grow with you.

Consider your woodworking budget.

Woodworking is no different from any other specialized hobby when it comes to budget-draining expenses. The price range for a table saw is truly wide open. If price and shop floor space were of no consequence, every woodworker would probably own a top-of-the-line cabinet saw. However, most budget-conscious woodworkers will find it difficult to justify paying the huge price of a professional-quality saw. Determine how a saw fits into the rest of the woodworking tool arsenal you still need to buy—routers, planers, jointers, sanders, band saws, power

If your woodworking requires a high degree of precision, especially if you frequently cut dadoes or raised panels, buy a saw that offers you smooth, solid performance with an amply powered induction motor of at least 1½ h.p.

miter saws, drill presses, lathes—the list goes on and on. Then buy as much bench-top, contractor's or cabinet saw as your budget allows. Don't discount the possibility of buying a used saw, either. For more information on buying a used versus new saw, see pages 20 to 22.

see pages 20 to 22.

The Bottom Line

For most woodworkers, a 10-in. contractor's saw with a 2-h.p. motor and precision rip fence is a sensible saw to buy. The table is large enough to handle workpieces of all sizes, and the under-carriage and arbor will handle the rigors of cutting with dado blades and molding heads. Since it's a middle-of-the-road saw, you'll be able to customize a contractor's saw as you like, with an assortment of aftermarket accessories.

You'll need a full-sized contractor's or cabinet saw for cutting sheet goods and other long stock safely. Either saw will give you the option of adding other helpful accessories later, like extension tables and precision rip fences.

Table Saw History

Table saw & horizontal borer all in one

The Egan Co. No. 3 Improved Variety Saw

Around 1902, this belt-driven cast-iron saw served double duty as a horizontal boring machine. As with other saws of its time, the saw table tilted, raised and lowered, while the saw arbor and blade remained fixed in place. A bit chuck, mounted to the opposite end of the arbor from the blade, was used for boring tasks. A separate drilling table on the right side of the saw could be raised or lowered in relation to the drill bit, then plunged forward into the bit to drill a hole.

Robland LX Combination Machine.

Multipurpose machines

A number of manufacturers offer woodworking machinery that combines several stationary tools in one unit. The table saw is the heart of these machines, configured with other tools like jointers, horizontal borers, planers, shapers and sanders. Some models have a single heavy-duty motor that is slid into different positions on the machine to power one tool at a time. Others incorporate several motors that work independently to run separate tools. The advantage to owning one of these multipurpose machines is that you can combine a shop's worth of stationary tools in one place. However, multipurpose machines are expensive, and the size of the table and fences for each tool might be limited. Spend some time using one of these machines, then try their individual stationary counterparts to see which approach will fit your woodworking needs best.

Buying a used saw

If purchasing a saw "fresh out of the box" isn't as important for you as getting the most for your money, consider purchasing a used table saw. You'll find used saws advertised in the classified ads of newspapers and woodworking magazines from time to time, as well as at auctions and garage or estate sales. Typically, the market for used table saws is quite good, so be aware that they may be difficult to find and may sell quickly. However, be persistent; aside from the amount of money you could save buying second-hand, there are a couple more compelling reasons to consider a used saw. First, buying used versus new may allow you to get a better quality saw for the same money. Second, well-cared-for table saws made by reputable manufacturers, especially saws with induction motors and cast-iron tables, arbors and cradle assemblies, are truly rugged tools with long lifespans. "Used" in no way implies "used up." You may need to replace a few belts or bearings on a 30-year-old saw, but you'll probably still come out ahead price-wise compared to buying a brand-new saw.

A host of hobbyist, professional, older and newer saws are available second-hand, as this used tool store proves. With some careful shopping and a bit of refurbishing, there's no reason a used saw can't perform as reliably and accurately as a new one—and possibly for a fraction of the cost.

Evaluating a used saw

Here are some components you'll want to inspect closely when diagnosing the condition of a used saw.

Saw table

Examine the saw table closely for hairline cracks. They may be difficult to see, and a magnifying glass can help. Cracks are an obvious indicator that the table has been subjected to some sort of trauma. It may have been removed from the saw and accidentally dropped. The saw may have tipped over during transport or could have been used as a makeshift workbench and damaged by a hammer blow. In any case, unless you know a qualified machine shop that can repair the crack, you're better off finding another saw. New saw tables are expensive and can be very difficult to locate for older models that are no longer made.

Carefully check the table for unevenness across the surface using a steel straightedge. It's impossible to do accurate work on a table saw that has an uneven tabletop. Check the saw table for flatness in all directions—lengthwise, widthwise and diagonally. NOTE: *Inspect how the extension wings are attached to the saw table when you're checking with a straightedge. It's common for the extension wings to be bolted slightly above or below the level of the center table, which will throw off*

your inspection. You can easily level the extension wings by repositioning or shimming the them (See pages 31 to 32).

Minor warping ($\frac{1}{16}$ in. or less across the saw table) can be corrected by having the table ground flat at a machine shop, although this might be expensive and can weaken the table. You can clean up other slight imperfections in the tabletop, like pitting from minor corrosion or scoring from fence and miter gauge wear and tear, by rubbing down the tabletop carefully with rubbing compound or naval jelly and a scrub pad (See page 46). Minor pitting and scoring is nothing to worry about and won't affect the saw's accuracy.

Arbor & bearings

Another area of concern when considering a used saw is the condition of the arbor and bearings. On good-quality saws with cast-iron and heavy-gauge steel mechanicals, it takes many years of hard use to generate significant wear, unless the saw was misused or subjected to moisture and allowed to rust.

To test the arbor, remove the throatplate and drive belts that connect the motor to the arbor so the arbor turns freely. Spin the blade by hand and listen (See bottom photo). If you hear any clicking or grinding sounds, the arbor bearings are worn. Rotate the arbor with your fingers and you'll feel the grittiness of pitted, grinding bearings. If the bearings are worn, they can be replaced or remanufactured by a good machine shop (they'll be tough to remove and install yourself without specialized bearing pullers and presses).

While you're at it, check the condition of the arbor shaft. It should be smooth and spin without noticeable wobble. Inspect the arbor shaft threads that hold the flange, blade, washer and nut in place. The threads should be clean and smooth.

NOTE: *In the case of direct-drive saws, the motor armature shaft is machined with threads on the end to serve as the saw's arbor. Use the same arbor tests to determine if the armature bearings are worn. Most better-quality electric motors can be serviced at reasonable prices. The presence of worn armature bearings isn't necessarily a reason to pass the saw up.*

Use a straightedge to examine the saw table for warpage as well as high and low areas. A dead-flat tabletop is critical to saw accuracy. You can correct minor warpage (less than 1⁄16 in. across the table), but avoid saws with more severe warping.

Inspect the inner V-faces of the pulleys that connect the drive belt or belts to the arbor and motor. Pulley faces should be clean, flat and smooth in the area where the belt rides. If the faces bow outward, the pulley or pulleys are worn and the belt will likely slip or burn when the saw is cutting under load. Don't worry if the pulleys are in good shape but the drive belts are cracked or worn; belts are inexpensive to replace. Replace belts with those recommended by the saw manufacturer. TIP: *If the saw has multiple drive belts, be sure to ask for "matched sets" when you order the belts. Matched sets will ensure that the circumferences match exactly, so the belts will wear evenly.*

Cradle, trunnions & worm gears

The cradle, trunnions and worm gears are responsible for supporting and moving the blade arbor. Since these parts move, eventually they will begin to wear. Here's how to evaluate their condition. Lay the saw on its side (or peer down through the throatplate opening). Inspect the condition of the handwheel worm gears and the gear teeth on the trunnions and arbor assembly. Look for uneven wear from tooth to tooth or

Check the arbor bearings for wear by removing the drive belt(s) (on contractor's and cabinet saws) and spinning the blade by hand. Listen for clicking and grinding, which are sure signs of bearing wear. Arbor bearings are fairly inexpensive to replace.

Check the condition of the worm gears and trunnions by cranking both handwheels over the full range of blade movement. The handwheels should turn smoothly, without binding.

Damaged throatplates are a telltale sign that the saw was abused or severely out of tune at some point. Scrutinize a saw with throatplate damage for other signs of neglect.

metal dust around these parts.

Stresses on these meshing parts, coupled with debris and grit that get thrown off the saw blade, can cause gears to wear or chip, especially if they aren't lubricated. (For more on periodic lubrication, see page 46.) Test the action of the gears by turning the hand wheels. The gears should mesh evenly, quietly and smoothly.

Other general considerations

Take a step back and look at the overall condition of a used saw. Inspect for signs of good saw maintenance and proper usage, including:
- minimal corrosion on metal parts
- the throatplate does not show signs of saw blade damage, an indicator that the saw has been severely out of tune, suffered kickback or some other severe blade trauma
- power cord and plug are free of cracks or frays
- rip fence slides smoothly and completely along the fence rails
- the saw isn't missing bolts, screws and other fasteners and these parts are tight

Ask the owner for the owner's manual that came with the saw, particularly if the saw is old. You might need it for ordering replacement parts later on.

Test drive before you buy

Finally, take the saw for a "test drive." The motor should start without hesitation, bring the blade up to speed quickly and have an even-sounding pitch when it reaches full power. If you can, make a few test cuts.

Does the motor labor excessively under loads? Does the saw vibrate noticeably when it's running or cutting? Does the saw cut cleanly and evenly or does it leave ragged, uneven cuts and burn marks? Many aspects of saw performance can be improved by simply tuning up the tool or installing a fresh blade. But consider that poor saw performance may be an indicator of the kind of general care the saw has been given by its owner over time.

Table Saw History

This guard and splitter assembly, patented by J. A. Fay & Co. in 1900, represents one of the first examples of table saw safety equipment available commercially. Notice that the guard covers the blade from above but not from the side, and it pivots up and down to ride on top of workpieces as they are passed through the blade. The guard, which undoubtedly was made of cast iron and steel, fastened to the splitter with a removable pin. Several holes on the splitter allowed the guard to be raised to accommodate thicker stock.

J. A. Fay & Co. guard and splitter assembly (circa 1900)

Safety

Table saws are wonderfully efficient and versatile tools, and they're capable of making nearly every straight cut you'll ever need for woodworking. But they have an inherent dark side. Regardless of how carefully you follow safety precautions, you can't change a tablesaw's basic characteristics. A standard table saw spins a 10-in.-dia. saw blade at around 4000 rpm, or about 120 mph. Every time you make a cut, the blade puts your hands and forearms at risk of injury, even when all of the saw's safety equipment is installed. This kind of blade velocity also generates a consider-able amount of dust and noise. Sawdust is irritating, especially if you have allergies, and the blade noise can be permanently debilitating over time.

The good news is, you can easily take measures to protect yourself. The following section covers personal safety items you should have on hand, proper workshop attire for sawing and other information related to table saw safety. Refer to the next chapter on "Making Basic Cuts," pages 56 to 97, for more information about those safety precautions you should take as you prepare to make and then execute specific kinds of cuts.

Use pushing tools & featherboards

As a rule, keep your hands as far from the spinning blade as you can without relinquishing control of the workpiece. Here are several simple devices for cutting safely:

A *pushstick* is simply a straight or curved handle, usually made of scrap wood, with a notch on the end for holding workpieces securely against the saw table.

Pushpads, commonly used with jointers, are rectangular plastic blocks with a handle on top and a non-skid lining. They spread workpiece control over a broader area when pushing boards facedown over the saw.

Pushing tools are inexpensive, but they are also easy to make. There's no specific formula for designing the best pushsticks, just a few general rules: you should be able to grip them comfortably; they should keep your hands far enough above the blade to be safely clear of it; and they should allow you to control the workpiece without feeling awkward.

Featherboards hold a workpiece snugly against the saw table and rip fence. They typically are made from a length of hardwood stock with a series of parallel 3- to 5-in.-long saw kerfs cut into one edge, forming springy "feathers" in the wood. You can make them easily in the shop (See *Tip,* next page), or you can buy inexpensive wood, plastic or magnetic-soled models.

Pushing tools for table saws. Plastic pushsticks (A) and pushpads (B) are inexpensive to buy, but simple wooden pushsticks (C) are easy to make. Keep a long-soled pusher (D) handy for providing broad support as well as a thin pusher (E) for squeezing into narrow spaces between the blade and rip fence.

Featherboards keep workpieces moving in the only safe direction: from front to back through the blade. Some featherboard designs incorporate a powerful magnet (A) to hold them tightly to the table. Other styles clamp to the rip fence (B), to the saw table (C) or pressure-fit by way of a short bar fitted into the miter slots (D).

Making featherboards

Select a length of hardwood scrap about 3 to 4 in. wide and 14 to 18 in. long. The length of the featherboard will depend on how far the featherboard must reach to the edge of the saw table for clamping purposes. Draw a line widthwise across the face of the board, about 5 in. from one end. Miter-cut the end of the board closest to this layout line at about a 40° angle (the angle can vary anywhere from 30° to 45°). Then, using a bandsaw or jig saw, make a series of parallel cuts from the angled end of the board to your layout line to form the flexible "feathers." Space the cuts evenly about ⅛ to ¼ in. apart.

Pull out the "Remove-to-lock" key every time you are finished using your saw. Without the key installed, the ON/OFF switch is locked, and you cannot turn on the machine. Keep the key in a safe place out of the reach of children.

Keep your senses sharp

Never operate a table saw while under the influence of alcohol or other drugs that make you drowsy, dull your senses or impair clear thought. It takes only a fraction of a second for sawing accidents to happen, so you have to focus your attention on what you are doing every time you make a cut. Think through the sequence of steps that will be required to perform a cutting operation before you begin, and keep in mind what your safe response should be when you encounter a problem (See *Chart,* page 68). Stop your work at the table saw if you find yourself starting to lose track of what you are doing or begin to feel frustrated or fatigued. Be particularly careful when you are making repetitive cuts; monotony leads to distraction, which invites accidents.

Dress appropriately

Wear comfortable, properly fitting rubber-soled shoes that give you good traction on your shop floor. Roll up your sleeves if they fit loosely, to keep them from getting caught on a workpiece or the saw blade. Keep pencils and other marking tools out of shirt pockets when sawing so they don't fall out and roll into the blade as you lean over the saw. Do not wear gloves while operating a table saw. You'll get a better grip on a workpiece if you manipulate it bare-handed, and your fingertips will warn you instantly if your feed rate changes or the board begins to behave erratically. Working without gloves means you may have to heat your shop in the wintertime to warm your hands, but extra warmth will keep the rest of your body's reflexes sharper and make your woodworking more comfortable anyway.

Unplug the saw whenever it is not being used

Simply switching the machine off isn't an adequate safety measure, especially when you are working on or near the blade and drive belt(s). Always unplug the saw for added insurance. It takes only a second to do, and it ensures that the saw cannot start again until you want it to.

Some saws are outfitted with "Remove-to-lock" keys that fit over a toggle-style ON/OFF switch. When the switch is in the off position, you can remove the key, making it impossible to flip the toggle switch back on. Remove and store this key in a safe place when you are not working in the shop to keep others—especially children—from starting the saw.

Use a heavy-duty extension cord plugged into a grounded outlet

Since table saws are mostly metal, be sure you choose a properly grounded three-prong outlet for powering the saw, and check the amperage of the circuit that supplies power to the outlet you'll use. Ideally, workshops should be wired with dedicated 20-amp circuits for 115-volt outlets and 40-amp circuits for 230-volt receptacles. Otherwise you'll likely trip the circuit when using the saw under full load.

Using an extension cord to power your saw can starve the motor of the amperage it requires to run properly, particularly if the extension cord is long or of too small a wire gauge. This condition, called *voltage drop,* results in the motor running slower and hotter than it should, which can lead to premature wear.

When you must use an extension cord, guard against voltage drop by selecting the shortest length of cord that will reach in a gauge heavy enough to provide at least the amperage your saw motor requires. Heavier-than-necessary gauges of extension cord are even better. Use the extension cord chart on this page as a guide to choosing the proper cord, and refer to your owner's manual to determine the motor amperage of your saw.

Extension cord ratings

To make certain that your table saw runs safely and at peak performance, check the amperage rating for your saw in your owner's manual. Use this chart as a guide for selecting the proper extension cord.

Cord Length	Gauge	Maximum Amps
25 ft.	18	10
25 ft.	16	13
25 ft.	14	15
50 ft.	16	10
50 ft.	14	15

Table Saw History

Gasoline-powered table saw

Parks Contractor's Special Portable Saw Rig (circa 1922)

The rise of internal combustion engines in the 1920s even influenced the table saw industry. For a time, Parks offered their swing-style ripping and crosscut saw with an optional gasoline engine. Intended no doubt for carpenters, this evolution toward self-powered table saws was a significant step away from either hand- or belt-driven power sources. The machine was advertised to be portable, despite its overall weight of a whopping 850 pounds.

Single-stage dust collector

POWERMATIC

Portable ambient air cleaner

RIDGID
AIR FILTRATION SYSTEM

CRAFTSMAN
AIRBORNE FILTRATION SYSTEM

Woodworkers Supply
OF NEW MEXICO

Woodworkers Supply
OF NEW HAMPSHIRE

shop·vac
10 GALLON THE ORIGINAL WET/DRY VACUUM
Shop vacuum

2.25

Ceiling-mounted ambient air cleaner

Powered dust collection devices are available for improving air quality in the shop. Single-stage dust collectors attach to stationary power tools through a system of flexible ductwork. A motor-driven impeller draws air through the duct-work and into replaceable collection bags. The bottom bag collects heavier saw-dust and chips, while the bag on top filters out finer dust. Ambient air cleaners use synthetic filters to trap fine, airborne dust that would escape a standard dust collector. Both portable and ceiling-mounted styles are available. A shop vacuum is handy for cleaning up excess sawdust in and around the saw.

Protect your lungs

Table saws generate large amounts of splinters and chips and clouds of fine sawdust, especially when they aren't connected to a dust collection system or are operated without the blade guard. Studies now indicate that sawdust can be a harmful irritant to mucous membranes in your nose and lungs, especially if you suffer from allergies or other respiratory problems. The dust from some wood species, such as Western red cedar, cocobolo and treated lumber can be particularly irritating or even hazardous to your health in concentrated amounts.

All of this is to say, protect your lungs from sawdust. If you use your saw frequently or in enclosed spaces, it's worth investing in a shop dust-collection system. Single- and two-stage dust collectors (See above photo) use a blower and a system of hoses and collection bags to draw dust and debris away from shop tools. Ambient air cleaners are free-standing or mount to the shop ceiling and draw air through a series of synthetic filters to remove fine, airborne sawdust.

If you choose not to install a dust-collection system, wear a dust mask. Many styles of dust masks are avail-

able and are rated safe for use in dusty conditions. The least expensive are the disposable paper particle masks. Choose the type with two straps rather than one to get a better seal around your nose and mouth. The more expensive, but better, mask varieties are the

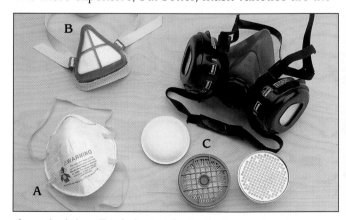

B

A

C

If you don't install a dedicated dust collection system, wear a dust mask instead, especially if you suffer from respiratory problems. Disposable particle masks (A) provide some protection, but a mask with replaceable filters (B) is even better. A cartridge style respirator (C) is your best line of defense against dust.

respirator-style silicone masks that use replaceable filter cartridges.

If you opt for a dust mask and not a dedicated dust-collection system, improve the air quality in the shop by providing for good ventilation. Open doors and windows or saw outside if the weather permits and your saw is portable. Set a fan in a window facing out to help draw dust out. The more fresh air that enters the shop, the better.

Protect your eyes & ears

Flying sawdust and splinters are hazardous to your eyes as well as your lungs. Not only can sawdust scratch your eyes, but it also impairs your vision when you are most vulnerable to bodily injury—in the middle of making a saw cut. Always wear eye protection when operating your table saw.

Prescription glasses are not safety glasses unless they have high-impact polycarbonate lenses. Even then, your eyes aren't fully protected from the top and sides. Choose a pair of safety glasses or goggles with anti-fog, anti-scratch and anti-static features, and that shield your eyes from all sides. Pick a style that fits your face comfortably, accommodates your prescription glasses if necessary, and hangs conveniently from a safety strap around your neck. The more comfortable and convenient your safety eyewear is, the more likely you'll be to wear it.

Table saws produce about 100 decibels of high-frequency noise, the kind of noise most likely to cause hearing loss. Hearing damage begins when your ears are subjected to noise frequencies higher than 85 decibels for extended periods of time. As with eye protection, do not underestimate the importance of adequate

When sawing, wear hearing protection **with a noise reduction rating of at least 25 decibels. Choose the most comfortable style for you: ear muffs (A), foam ear inserts (B) or ear bands (C).**

hearing protection in the shop, even if you use your saw only occasionally. Pick a style of hearing protection most comfortable for you. You'll find three essential types: ear muffs, ear inserts and ear bands. Ear muffs completely cover your ears and wrap around the top of your head. Ear inserts are small foam cylinders, either loose or attached to one another with a length of plastic cord, that you roll between your fingers and insert into your ear canals. The foam expands to block out noise. Ear bands are made of flexible plastic and are outfitted on either end with a plastic cone or foam pad that inserts into or covers your ear canals. The band wraps around the back of your head or hangs from your chin to help hold the earplugs in place. Any of these three hearing protection types you choose will block out the harmful high-frequency noise, but still allow you to hear ordinary conversation. Be sure that the ear protection you wear for sawing has a noise reduction rating (NRR) of at least 25 decibels.

Prepare for emergencies

Install a first-aid kit in the shop within clear view. Should a table saw accident occur, you'll need a first-aid kit suitable for treating lacerations, amputations and eye injuries. Learn the proper techniques for stopping bleeding, treating eye injuries and handling the kind of shock associated with severe injury. Install a telephone in your shop and keep a list of emergency phone numbers posted close by. Let someone know you're working in the shop and have him or her check up on you from time to time, especially if your shop occupies an outbuilding out of range of earshot. Finally, equip your shop with a fire extinguisher rated to handle both electrical and combustible fires.

Most woodworkers would rather be cutting boards than taking time out to tune up and maintain their table saws. While it's true that adjusting your rip fence isn't as much fun as ripping a piece of cherry accurately and safely, you really can't have one without the other. That is, don't expect precise and pleasurable cutting from a saw that needs a tune-up.

If you're not the type who enjoys fiddling with machines, the good news is that a number of the tune-up procedures outlined in this chapter only need to be done once when your saw is new and then infrequently after that. The tuning chores you'll need to do more frequently can be taken care of in about an hour.

If you are uncrating and assembling your saw for the first time, don't assume the saw comes tuned up straight from the factory. No saw does. The saw's mechanical components, especially the motor and hand controls, were probably tested before the saw was packaged, but the saw probably wasn't fully assembled, tuned, and then disassembled. The owner's manual that comes with your new saw will provide instructions for putting the saw together correctly, but few manufacturers take you through the next important step of fine-tuning your saw.

All saws will eventually fall out of adjustment after cutting wood for a while and require a tune-up. It's unavoidable. Tune-ups are required most frequently on lower-quality saws, heavily used saws and saws that get moved around the shop often. It doesn't take much

jostling to throw a splitter or rip fence out of alignment. It's also a good idea to check the tuning on a saw you haven't used for some time or are using as a guest. Treat an unfamiliar saw as though it has never been tuned. You'll safeguard yourself and ensure more accurate cutting right from the start.

Follow the procedures outlined in this chapter to give your saw a thorough going-over before you start that first woodworking project. You'll most certainly get better cutting results.

Watch for tune-up clues

A saw will exhibit several clues if it's due for a tune-up. Watch for changes on the cut edges of your workpieces. Look for increasing numbers of circular blade swirls or burn marks on the wood. Also check a workpiece after you rip it to see if the long edges are exactly parallel. At the same time, check to see that the edges are square to the board faces. They should be. If not, make some more test cuts and inspect the results. Consistently sloppy cuts indicate that your saw isn't cutting as it should.

Another possible indicator that your saw needs tuning is if the blade smokes or stalls in mid-cut. Smoke indicates that the blade is generating excessive heat and burning the wood. You need to fix this problem to keep from taxing the saw motor, dulling or warping the blade, scorching your workpiece and as a safety precaution to prevent kickback.

Telltale signs that it's time for a tune-up

Increasing numbers of burn marks **on workpieces is a sign that the blade and rip fence are out of alignment or the blade is dirty or dull. Be aware that some kinds of woods like cherry are prone to burns when you cut them, even if your saw is in tune.**

Draw a line along a workpiece **and rip-cut the board along your layout line. Does the blade follow your line? If it begins to drift, your blade could be heeling (See pages 36 to 37) or the fence needs to be adjusted so it's parallel to the blade.**

Tools you'll need for saw tune-ups

A basic tool kit for tune-ups includes: **(A) 4- to 6-ft. steel straightedge; (B) Dial indicator with magnetic base; (C) Combination square; (D) Soft-faced or rubber mallet; (E) Flat file; (F) 3-ft. straightedge; (G) Allen wrenches; (H) Standard and metric wrenches; (I) Screwdrivers; (J) Felt-tipped marker; (K) Fine-grit sharpening stone; (L) Try square; (M) Drafting square; (N) Speed square.**

Once you become comfortable using your saw, you'll acquire a sixth sense for noticing when cutting just isn't right. Trust your instincts. The more wood you cut, the more accustomed you'll become to the particular sound the blade makes as you cut different kinds of wood. You'll also get a "feel" for the right speed to push wood through the blade (called *feed rate*). If the saw motor begins to bog down in a type of wood you cut regularly, a quick tune-up or a fresh, sharp blade likely will solve the problem. A tune-up is also in order if you notice the saw vibrating more than usual or making more noise.

By all means, inspect your saw carefully and tune it up if you experience kickback (See page 71). Kickback indicates one of three possible problems: You are sawing unsafely; your lumber is defective and unsuitable for the table saw; or the blade and rip fence aren't in proper alignment.

Before you cut another board, evaluate what's unusual about what you were doing when the kickback occurred. If you are confident that your cutting techniques are correct, and the troubles you are having aren't due to defective lumber (See page 59), it's time for a saw tune-up.

Tune-up goals

Tuning a table saw boils down to correcting four simple geometric relationships between the miter slots, blade, fences and saw table. On a properly tuned saw, the table will be flat across its entire surface, including the extension wings. Second, the blade and rip fence must both be parallel to the miter slots. When this is true, the blade and rip fence will be parallel to one another as well. Third, the blade, rip fence and miter gauge fence should be square (perpendicular) to the saw table. A fourth goal is to minimize sources of saw vibration. The usual culprits for vibration are a dirty or dull blade, excessive blade and arbor runout or misaligned arbor and motor pulleys. If your saw still cuts poorly after satisfying these four goals, you may be using an underpowered saw for the task at hand.

Tune-up checklist

How frequently you tune your saw will depend on many variables, including the quality of your saw and how often and rigorously you use it. Refer to the following tune-up chart and timelines as a general guide:

✔ Clean the saw	After each use
✔ Adjust the rip fence to the miter slots	Periodically
✔ Adjust the splitter and antikickback pawls	Periodically
✔ Inspect and remedy other sources of vibration	As needed
✔ Set the blade tilt stops	Monthly
✔ Tune the miter gauge	Monthly
✔ Clean saw blades and protect from rust	Monthly
✔ Flatten the tabletop and extension wings	Annually
✔ Align the blade to the miter slots	Annually
✔ Align the motor and arbor pulleys	Annually

Flatten the tabletop

Since many of the tune-up procedures explained in this chapter involve the saw table in one way or another, it makes sense to start your general saw tune-up here. Unless the saw table is flat, workpieces won't rest evenly and in turn won't meet the blade squarely when you cut them.

Start your tabletop tune-up by examining the center cast-metal portion of the saw table for warpage (also called *wind*). To do this, you'll use a simple set of devices called *winding sticks*, which are nothing more than two flat hardwood sticks about 18 to 20 in. long, with widths that match. Set the sticks on-edge along opposite edges of the center saw table. Position yourself about 1 ft. from the stick closer to you and adjust your line of sight across the top edge of this stick, looking beyond it to the opposite stick. If the saw table is warped, the top edges of the back stick won't line up evenly with the top edges of the front stick. Check the center table with winding sticks both widthwise and depth-wise (See *Illustration,* right).

A warped cast-iron saw table usually indicates that the metal was not allowed to cure properly when the table was manufactured. If your saw is new and under warranty, return the saw. Otherwise, you may be able to correct minor warpage by inserting metal shims at one or more corners where the saw table bolts to the base. Shimming is most effective if the center table is made of a softer metal alloy, such as those found on many benchtop saws. Your other alternative is to have the saw table ground flat at a machine shop—a much pricier fix.

The tabletop tune-up tasks will require using a perfectly flat straightedge about 4 to 6 ft. long. A precision-ground steel straightedge is best, but a good one will cost more than $100. A much cheaper but sufficiently reliable alternative

Using winding sticks. Check the center cast-iron portion of the saw table for warp with a pair of hardwood winding sticks. Set the sticks along the edges of the saw table and inspect the table across its width (A), then across its depth (B).

Tabletop warpage less than 1/16 in. across the surface may be correctable by inserting thin metal shims underneath one or more corners of the saw table, where it bolts to the saw base. Your odds for correcting warp in this way improve if the saw table is made of softer, more flexible aluminum alloys. For more severe warp, replace the saw table or have it reground at a machine shop.

is to make a straightedge instead. Build one from a dimensionally stable material like MDF (medium-density fiberboard), solid-core plywood or seasoned hardwood, and flatten the edges on a jointer.

To check the table, drag your long straightedge on-edge in all directions, checking for dips or

rises in the surface. Check carefully; these high and low spots will be slight. You'll be able to see any imperfections easily by shining a light behind the straightedge and looking for slivers of light that appear between the edge of the straightedge and the table surface. Circle high areas on the tabletop with a marker or grease pencil and use a fine-grit sharpening stone or wet-dry sandpaper to flatten them out. The goal here is to just even out high and low areas, so proceed carefully, and remove as little metal as possible.

Once you're satisfied that the center table is flat, lay your straightedge across the joints between the center table and both extension wings. To flatten these two long joints, slightly loosen the mounting bolts that hold the extension wings in place, then tap the extension wings up or down with a soft-faced mallet or a hammer and wood block until the surfaces are flush. Retighten the bolts and check the joints again with a square. TIP: *Your saw should come with lock-washers on the mounting bolts to hold the extension wings fast. If it doesn't, pick up some lockwashers at a hardware store and insert them between each nut and bolt before you adjust the extension wing joints. Lockwashers will keep the nuts and bolts tight so the joints won't shift.*

Check the entire saw table for flatness by laying the straightedge

Drag a long straightedge **over the center cast portion of the saw table to identify high and low areas. Then, check the joints between the center table and the extension wings. If the joints are uneven, loosen the extension wing bolts and tap the joints flush with a rubber mallet.**

across the full tabletop. Check to see that the extension wings don't bow up or down from the center table. If they do, and your extension wings are made of pressed steel, loosen the bolts that fasten them to the fence rails, pull the extension wings up or down to flatten them and retighten the bolts. If

the extension wings are made of cast-iron or another solid metal alloy, you'll have to use thin plastic or metal shims in the joints to tip the wings up or down. Bolt the wings tightly to the center table again with the shims in place. Trim the shims flush.

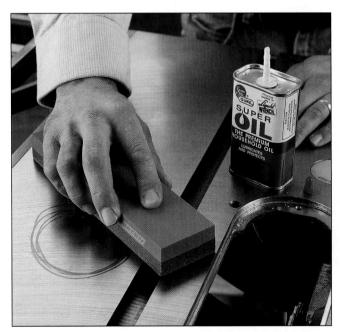

Circle high areas **on the saw table, then carefully grind them flat with a fine-grit sharpening stone lubricated with water or fine-grade machine oil. Try to remove as little metal as possible— your goal is to just even out these surface irregularities.**

Shimming extension wings. **If your saw has cast extension wings and they tilt up or down, flatten them to the saw table by inserting paper shims into the joint between the extension wing and the center table.**

Adjust the throatplate

The last step in flattening the saw table is to adjust the removable throatplate. Most saw throatplates have four allen screws that adjust the throatplate up and down to sit flush with the table surface. On some saws, these setscrews may actually fasten the throatplate to the saw table.

Regardless of which throatplate type your saw has, a flush fit with the top of the table is important. A flush throatplate won't snag workpieces as they are fed into the blade, and it won't allow wood to catch on the back edge of the throatplate as workpieces exit the blade. Check to see if your throatplate needs adjustment by laying a short straightedge across the throatplate and shining a flashlight along the edge where the throatplate meets the straightedge. Adjust the throatplate setscrews until the sliver of light disappears. Be sure the throatplate is flush with the saw table both widthwise and lengthwise.

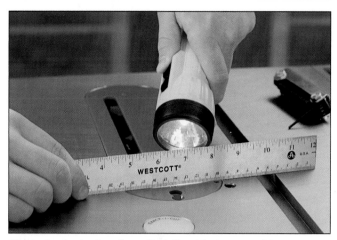

Check the throatplate for a flush fit with the saw table by shining a light behind a steel rule laid over the throatplate. Any sliver of light that appears beneath the rule indicates that the throatplate is set too low. To adjust, turn the setscrews. Light that shows between the rule and the table means the throatplate is too high.

Option: Replace, rather than adjust, your throatplate

The trouble with most standard throatplates is that the slot for the blade is too wide. Wide gaps around the blade will cause the blade to splinter some woods (called *tearout*) because the wood isn't supported next to the blade. Rather than shearing the wood cleanly, the blade begins to tear the wood fibers as it cuts. Another problem with wide blade slots is that narrow scraps of wood can actually get lodged in the slot between the throatplate and the spinning saw blade. If a substantial scrap should catch on the blade teeth, the

blade could throw the cut-off scrap back toward you. A good solution to these problems is to install a shop-built throatplate with a blade opening that's only slightly wider than the thickness of your blade—commonly called a *zero-clearance throatplate*. They're easy to make. Here's how:

Select a scrap of hardwood that's larger than the throatplate opening in your saw table and thicker than the throatplate recess in the saw table. You can also purchase plastic throatplate blanks from woodworking

How to make a zero-clearance throatplate

1 Plane a length of hardwood to a thickness that matches the depth of the throatplate recess in your saw table. Use the factory throatplate as a template for tracing the throatplate shape onto your hardwood blank. Trim the blank to shape with a band saw or scroll saw, and sand the cut edges smooth.

2 With the saw blade lowered, set the new throatplate blank into the saw table recess. Clamp a piece of scrap wood on top of the throatplate to hold it in place. Turn on the saw and crank the blade up slowly until it cuts through the throatplate. Raise the blade to full height.

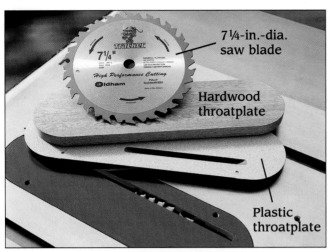

7¼-in.-dia. saw blade

Hardwood throatplate

Plastic throatplate

Build your own zero-clearance throatplates from scrap hardwood, or buy a preformed plastic throatplate blank from a woodworking supply house. Aftermarket plastic throatplates come shaped to fit specific saws, and some, like the one shown here, have a slot cut partway through to make room for the blade. You may need to install a smaller 7¼-in.-dia. circular blade on your saw in order to cut the initial kerf opening, if your 10-in.-dia. blade doesn't drop below the saw table far enough to clear the bottom of the zero-clearance throatplate. Case in point: the blade installed in the saw shown here is lowered as far as it will go, and it barely clears the bottom of the red throatplate.

supply catalogs that are shaped to fit a variety of different saws (See photo, left, and page 8). If you choose to make your own hardwood throatplate, plane the wooden blank so it matches the exact depth of the throatplate recess in the saw table.

Use the original throatplate that came with your saw as a template to draw the throatplate shape onto your hardwood blank. Cut out the throatplate shape with a band saw or scroll saw and smooth the edges with a sander.

If the throatplate on your saw fastens to the saw table with screws, drill countersunk pilot holes in the wood throatplate for the screws so the screw heads will sit below the surface of the throatplate once it is installed on the saw.

Since the goal of a zero-clearance throatplate is to match the throatplate opening to the blade thickness, use the saw blade to cut its own blade slot in the throatplate. First, raise the blade to full height and square it to the saw table. Then, crank the blade all the way below the saw table and set the zero-clearance throatplate in place.

If the blade won't clear the throatplate from below, which is commonly the case, you'll have to install a smaller-diameter blade in the saw to start the kerf cut. On most saws, a 7¼-in. circular saw blade with an ⅛-in. kerf will do the trick, but be sure the thickness of the blade matches the kerf of the larger blade you plan to use with the throatplate. Hold down the throatplate by positioning a board over the throatplate and clamping the board to the saw table. Start the saw and raise the blade slowly until it cuts through the surface of the throatplate. Lower the blade again, unplug the saw and change to your larger diameter saw blade. Finish cutting the kerf opening in the throatplate by raising the blade gradually through the throatplate to its full height.

Don't toss your old throatplate

Here are a couple things to keep in mind when using zero-clearance throatplates: You won't be able to tilt the blade with a zero-clearance throatplate in place. The narrow kerf will obstruct the blade as it tilts on the trunnions, so switch back to your original throatplate when making bevel cuts. Second, you may need to make several throatplates if you routinely use different blades—blade kerf widths may vary by blade type and manufacturer.

Single-use throatplates

A quick alternative to building zero-clearance throatplates is to simply clamp a piece of tempered hardboard or ¼- to ½-in.-thick plywood to the saw table over the throatplate area. Raise the blade until it cuts through the scrap board. Be sure to use a piece long enough to extend across the depth of the saw table and wide enough to support the workpieces you are cutting. Keep your hands clear as you cut the kerf.

Check blade & miter slot alignment

For all-around accurate cutting, it's not enough that the rip fence and blade are parallel with one another. The blade must also be parallel to the miter slots. If it isn't, the blade will make skewed crosscuts when you are using the miter gauge, because it won't be cutting in a plane that's perpendicular to the miter gauge. When the blade isn't parallel to the miter slots, the condition is called *blade heel* (See *Tip,* next page).

Although blade heel is a common problem on new saws that have never been tuned, it's not something you can see without careful inspection. If the blade is off by even 1/32 in. from front to back, it will affect how the saw cuts. Once you've corrected for blade heel, you'll probably never need to adjust for heel again unless the saw is disassembled.

When tuning your table saw, use the miter slots as your standard of reference for aligning both the blade and the rip fence. This way, not only will the blade and rip fence be parallel with the miter slots, they also will be parallel with one another.

To test for blade heel, unplug the saw, then raise the blade to full height. Set a try square on the saw table and against the saw blade body. Be sure the square isn't touching the carbide blade teeth; the square must sit flat against the blade body. Crank the blade-tilt handwheel one way or the other until the blade is square to the table. If the handwheel stops before you reach the point where the blade is square, see "Setting blade tilt stops," page 38.

Next, lay a long metal straightedge against the blade body. NOTE: *A 2-ft. straightedge will work for most saws, but it is better to use one that stretches across the full depth of your saw table. It's important that the straightedge be absolutely flat along its edge, because it will establish the exact geometric plane of the blade relative to the miter slots. You'll use the straightedge to measure and compare the distances between the blade and a miter slot on both the infeed (front) and outfeed (back) ends of the saw table. The further away from the blade you take your measurements, the more exaggerated the differences in measurements will be, so you'll be able to detect even the slightest heeling.* With the straightedge in position, choose a block of wood that is about 1 1/2 in. wide by 3 ft. long and fits snugly into the miter slot. Set the wood block into either miter slot.

Rest the head of a combination square against the the straightedge near the infeed edge of the saw table. Extend the rule on the square until it touches the wood block and lock the rule in place. Then set the combination square against the straightedge near the back of the saw. Does the end of the rule just touch the wood block? If it comes up short or long, your blade is heeling. To correct the blade heel, see pages 36 to 37.

1 To check for blade and miter slot alignment, start by raising the blade to full height and squaring it to the table with a try square. The square should touch the blade body, not the teeth.

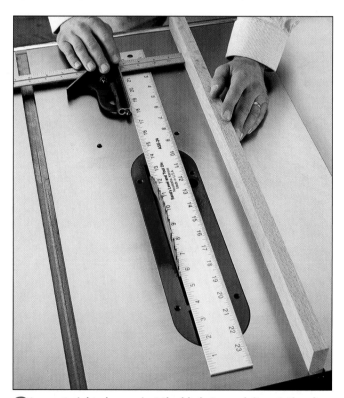

2 Lay a straightedge against the blade to mark its rotational plane. Set a piece of scrap wood into the miter slot (it should fit snugly). Set a combination square against the straightedge and slide the rule until it touches the scrap. Take a reading at the front and back of the saw table. The measurements should match; if not, the blade is heeling.

Understanding blade heel

When the blade isn't parallel with the miter slots, the condition is called *heel*. A blade that "heels" will cut at an angle to both the miter gauge and the rip fence, so both rip cuts and crosscuts will be inaccurate. Blade heel is hazardous in ripping situations when the outfeed side of the blade heels toward the rip fence. In this instance, every time you make a rip cut, you are essentially forcing your workpiece into a funnel, which binds the workpiece between the fence and the blade, increasing your chances for kickback. The trouble with heeling on the infeed side is that the blade will pull the workpiece away from the fence. In either case of heel, the blade actually cuts twice—on both the upstroke and the downstroke. Cutting twice heats up the blade, resulting in burned edges on your work.

Infeed heeling occurs when distance A is shorter than distance B. The blade will tend to pull workpieces away from the rip fence.

Outfeed heeling forces workpieces into a narrower opening at the back of the blade. Distance B is shorter than distance A.

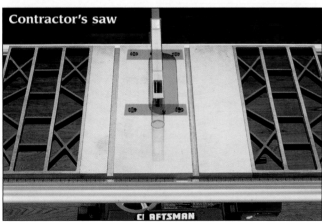

The shaded areas and dark circles on these saws **represent the locations of the bolts you'll need to loosen in order to correct a heeling blade. Once the bolts are loosened on a cabinet saw, shift the whole saw table to realign the miter slots with the blade. On a contractor's saw, loosen the bolts and shift the trunnions instead.**

Correcting blade heel

To correct infeed or outfeed blade heel, you'll need to shift the position of the arbor relative to the saw table. The process for making this adjustment varies, depending upon how the arbor mounts to the saw. On most cabinet saws, the arbor assembly bolts to the saw cabinet, not the saw table. To shift the arbor, locate the bolts that hold the saw table to the cabinet and loosen all but one slightly. (Usually there are four bolts.) Then, tap the saw table until the blade is parallel to the miter slots. You may need to loosen the fourth bolt a touch to make pivoting easier.

On contractor's and direct-drive benchtop saws, as well as some smaller cabinet saws, the arbor assembly bolts to the saw table, not the saw base. You'll need to loosen three of the four bolts that secure the trunnions to the underside of the saw table. Tap the cradle assembly from behind one way or the other, with a hammer and wood block to shift the arbor and blade into alignment with the miter slots. NOTE: *You may be able to gain better access to the cradle assembly by reaching through the throatplate opening.* Regardless of the saw type, work carefully and check your progress against the combination square and rule. Once you find the correct arbor position, retighten the bolts evenly.

A good dynamic test to check your blade alignment is to simply listen for signs of heeling. To do this, first be sure the bar on your miter gauge fits snugly in the miter slot (See page 39). Remove the saw's drive belt(s). Clamp a length of scrap wood to the miter gauge fence so the blade teeth just graze the scrap when you spin

How to adjust trunnions

Once you've loosened the trunnion bolts on a contractor's saw, use a hammer and wood block to move the entire trunnion assembly to the right or left. Doing so will alter the blade's relationship to the miter slots, which is necessary if the blade is heeling. Rap lightly and check your progress often.

Option: Depending upon the make of your saw, you may be able to gain better access to the trunnion assembly by working through the throatplate opening in the saw table.

the blade by hand. Raise the blade to full height. Slide the miter gauge to the infeed side of the blade and spin the blade hard. Listen to the sound the blade makes as it rubs against the scrap. If the sound is even all around, you've corrected blade heel. If the pitch changes, determine the area of the blade where the change occurs and mark a blade tooth in this area with chalk or a felt-tipped marker.

Slide the miter gauge and scrap to the outfeed side of the blade and spin the blade again. If the blade area you marked grazes the scrap and makes the same noise as it did when you tested on the infeed side, you've corrected the heeling condition, but the blade is warped in the area you've marked. If the sound is louder or softer in the marked area than it was when you tested on the infeed side, the blade is still heeling.

Continue your adjustments until the blade no longer heels. If it seems your blade is warped, check the amount of warpage (called *runout*) with a dial indicator (See pages 44 to 45).

Check your heeling adjustments by spinning the blade and allowing it to rub against a wood block clamped to the miter gauge. Set the block near the front of the blade, spin the blade and listen. Then slide the miter gauge and scrap to the back of the blade and spin. If the pitch you hear is consistent all around, the blade is no longer heeling. If the rubbing sound gets louder or softer, mark the area on the blade where the pitch changes. Changes in pitch likely indicate that the blade is still heeling.

Tilt adjustment options

The location of blade tilt stops, **which help set 45° and 90° blade tilt settings, varies from saw to saw. On this contractor's saw, one stop is mounted on a stabilizer bar on the cradle assembly, and the other stop is situated at the end of the front trunnion. Check your owner's manual to locate the stops on your saw.**

Table-mounted tilt stops. **Some manufacturers make the process of setting blade tilt easier by mounting the stop screws in the saw table rather than underneath. To adjust blade tilt, align the blade to a drafting triangle or try square and turn the stop screws until you feel resistance.**

Setting blade tilt stops

Most table saw cuts take place with the blade set at either 90° or 45° to the saw table. To help speed the process of setting these angles, better-quality saws are equipped with adjustment screws or bolts, called *tilt stops,* that limit the path of the trunnions as they tilt. When the tilt stops are correctly set, you should feel resistance in the handwheel when the pointer on the blade tilt scale reaches the 90° and 45° marks on the scale. If you can't reach either blade angle before the handwheel stops turning, or if you can crank past these marks, one or both tilt stops need adjustment.

To set the 90° stop, crank the blade to full height, lay a try square against the blade body and adjust for square. Check your owner's manual to locate the 90° tilt stop (usually located on the end of the front trunnion). The stop may be a simple setscrew or a bolt and nut. Turn the stop in or out until the handwheel stops the blade at 90°. Set the 45° blade stop in the same fashion. This stop may be located near the 90° stop on the trunnion or on the opposite end of the trunnion altogether. Check your owner's manual to be sure. Use a 45° drafting square or a speed square to set the blade to precisely 45° on the saw table before you adjust the stop.

A few saw manufacturers simplify the job of adjusting the blade stops by recessing allen screws into the saw table near the throatplate. The allen screw system replaces the standard stops located on the trunnions, so you can adjust the blade without reaching under the saw table. One allen screw sets the 90° blade stop and the other screw sets the 45° stop. To adjust the blade tilt, crank the blade to either 90° or 45°, check the blade setting with a square or triangle and turn the allen screw until you feel resistance.

Once you've established accurate 90° and 45° blade stops, reset the blade tilt pointer on the front of the saw so the scale reads accurately when the blade is tilted to each stop. NOTE: *You may have to remove a handwheel to adjust the pointer.* As a rule, use the blade tilt scale to "ballpark" your blade angle settings. Don't rely on the blade tilt scale for setting precise blade angles. Where accuracy is important, always set and check your blade angle against a truing instrument—a bevel gauge set to the angle you want, a drafting triangle or a square—before you make your cut. Then cut a test piece first to verify your accuracy.

Dynamic test for checking 90° tilt setting

1 Once you've adjusted your 90° blade tilt stop, check the setting for accuracy by cross-cutting a piece of scrap using the miter gauge as a guide. Mark the face of the scrap first to keep the orientation of the parts clear once you cut it in two.

2 Flip the cutoff piece over and set the cut edges together on the saw table. If the tilt stop is set accurately, the cut edges should meet flush. If a gap appears, it is double the amount the blade is off of 90°. Adjust your 90° tilt stop and test again.

Dynamic test for checking 45° tilt setting

1 Conduct a similar dynamic test as the one outlined above to check your 45° blade tilt setting. Tilt the blade until it stops at 45°. Mark one face of a piece of scrap and cross-cut it with the workpiece held against the miter gauge.

2 Flip one of the cut edges and set the scrap pieces together to form a mitered corner. If the 45° blade tilt stop is set accurately, the scrap pieces should form a 90° corner. If they don't, adjust the tilt stop and try the dynamic test again.

Align the rip fence & miter slots

Once you've adjusted the blade so it's parallel to the miter slots and square to the table, do the same for the rip fence. Set a pair of 1½-in.-wide wood blocks into a miter slot, one near the front and one near the rear of the saw table. The blocks should fit snugly in the miter slot. Slide the rip fence until it rests against one or both of the blocks. If the fence is parallel to the miter slot, it should touch both blocks. Otherwise, the fence needs to be adjusted.

Depending upon the style, adjusting your saw's rip fence involves loosening two bolts located on either the top or the outside face of the fence body. Refer to your owner's manual to locate these adjustment bolts. Loosen them and shift the fence body to the left or right until the fence touches both wood blocks at the same time. Then retighten the bolts and check the alignment again. If your fence works properly (and some may not), you should be able to slide the fence anywhere along the fence rails and lock it down parallel to the blade. Be aware that not all fences are created equal. Some fences are chronically difficult to keep tuned. If your fence is one of these, you may want to consider buying a replacement fence. For more on replacement fences, see pages 132 to 133.

Since the rip fence gets moved frequently and even removed, it's a good idea to spot-check your fence alignment from time to time. Save the miter slot wood blocks for future testing.

To align your rip fence to a miter slot, **slip a couple of scrap blocks into a miter slot. The block should fit snugly. Slide the rip fence up to the blocks. If the fence doesn't touch both blocks, loosen the adjustment bolts on the rip fence, tap the fence body until it touches the blocks, and tighten the bolts.**

Square the rip fence to the saw table

When a rip fence is locked down to the table, the face of the fence should be perpendicular to the saw table. Otherwise, workpieces won't sit flat against the fence and square with the blade. Test how close to perpendicular your fence is to the saw table using a try square. Some better-quality fences will have setscrews to help you make this adjustment (See photo, left), but most fences will not. If your fence has no setscrews and it isn't square to the table, you may have to attach an auxiliary wood fence to the rip fence and shim it to square (See photo, right).

How to square a rip fence

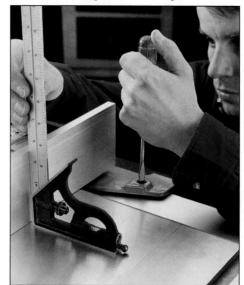

Some rip fences have setscrews **that allow you to square the fence to the saw table. On these fences, set a square against the fence and turn the screws in or out until the fence rests flush against the square.**

If your rip fence has no adjustment screws for squaring it to the table, attach an auxiliary wood fence to the rip fence, and insert paper shims until the wood fence is square to the saw table.

Tuning the miter gauge

A miter gauge is essentially a sliding crosscut fence for your saw. To be precise, the miter gauge bar needs to slide along the miter slots smoothly and without side-to-side play. You can also adjust the protractor head for accuracy at both 90° and 45° if your gauge comes with stop screws at these angle settings.

Adjust the fence on the miter gauge to 90° by positioning a combination square against the miter bar and the fence. If your miter gauge comes equipped with an adjustable stop screw for 90°, loosen the locknut that holds the tiny screw in place and turn the screw in or out until it rests against the flip-up stop. Set the 45° adjustable stop in the same fashion, using a speed square or plastic drafting square to establish the angle of the protractor head.

To test the miter gauge bar, set it in a miter slot and try to wiggle it from side to side. It's common for the bar to be slightly undersized for the miter slot. The miter gauge bar will loosen in the slot as it wears from sliding back and forth in the miter slot. You can improve the fit of the miter bar easily by tapping pairs of dimples along either bar edge with a hammer and center punch. Space the dimples every inch or so along the full length of the bar. Try the fit of the bar in the slot; if it doesn't fit in the miter slot or drags when you slide it back and forth, knock down the ridges of the dimples slightly with a fine metal file.

Tightening loose miter bars

Take the slop out of your miter gauge's slide by punching a series of dimples along the edges of the miter bar with a metal punch and a ball-peen hammer. If the bar fits too tightly after you do this, file the tops of the dimples down slightly. The bar should slide smoothly without side play.

1 Use a combination square as a guide to set the miter gauge fence so it is 90° to the metal bar that slides in the miter slots. Rest the head of the square against the bar and the rule against the fence.

2 Most miter gauges have stop screws that allow you to set the fence to 90° or 45° quickly. Tip the flip stop up and turn the 90° stop screw until it touches the flip stop. Then pivot the miter fence against a drafting triangle, set the fence for 45° and adjust the 45° stop screw against the flip stop as well.

ANTIKICKBACK PAWLS
REMOVED FOR CLARITY

To adjust most splitters, sandwich the saw blade between two straightedges. If the splitter is out of alignment, loosen the bolts that secure the splitter to the saw, and shift the splitter until it touches neither of the straightedges. Retighten the splitter bolts.

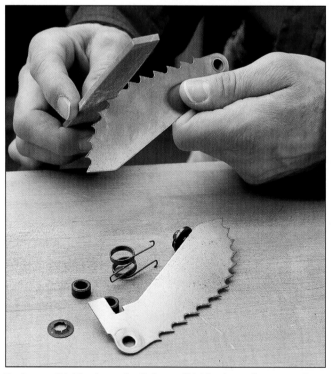

Tuning antikickback pawls. If the antikickback pawls mounted on your saw's splitter fail to grab your workpieces, you may be able to improve pawl performance by sharpening the teeth with a file. If this doesn't help, set the entire splitter lower on the saw table, or buy stiffer springs to hold the pawls in place.

Tune the splitter & antikickback pawls

Splitters need to line up perfectly behind the blade, or they'll hang up workpieces as wood exits the blade. Splitters that come as standard table saw equipment are made of a piece of sheet metal, which can be adjusted to the left or right behind the blade. Here's how: Loosen the nuts that hold the splitter/guard assembly to the back of the saw. NOTE: *Some better-quality saws will also have an adjustable mounting plate beneath the throatplate on the cradle assembly that holds the front of the splitter in place. You may need to loosen the bolts on this mounting plate as well.* Set two straightedges against the blade body (not against the carbide teeth) on either side. Shift the splitter until it sits between, but does not touch, either straightedge. Retighten the splitter mounting bolts.

Test the effectiveness of your antikickback pawls by making a rip cut down the center of a piece of ¾-in.-thick scrap about 3 ft. long. Stop the cut and shut off the saw when about 1 ft. of the workpiece has passed through the blade. Unplug the saw and lower the blade. Grab hold of the workpiece on the infeed side of the blade and try to pull it back toward yourself. If you can pull the workpiece backwards out of the cut, the anti-kickback pawls need tuning. By design, the pawls should drag along the top of the workpiece as it passes through the blade from front to back but dig into the wood if kickback occurs.

The bottom edges of the antikickback pawls should sit as close to the saw table as possible when not in use. The best scenario is that the tips of the pawl teeth actually touch the saw table. On some saws, the pawls may float ¼ in. or more off the table, which renders them useless for protecting you from kicked-back stock that is less than ¼ in. thick. You may need to modify how the splitter mounts to the saw so the pawls will rest closer to or against the saw table. Elongating the splitter bolt holes may do the trick, in order for the entire splitter to sit lower on the saw table.

If the pawls touch the table but they still allow you to slide workpieces back out of the cut, the problem may be that the points on the pawls are too dull to "bite" into the wood. To remedy the problem, remove the pawls and sharpen the points with a flat file, then reinstall the pawls on the splitter. The pawls may also be outfitted with springs that are too weak to hold the pawls firmly against the workpiece. If this is the case, install stiffer springs.

You may be able to replace the splitter and antikickback pawls on your saw with a better-quality, removable splitter, especially if you own a popular-model contractor's or cabinet saw. For more on aftermarket splitters, see page 135.

Reducing saw vibration

A saw that vibrates excessively will produce rougher cuts than one that runs smoothly. This is because vibration makes the blade flex back and forth as it spins on the arbor, so the blade makes wider, uneven cuts. Over time, vibration can also loosen fasteners and other parts on the saw, but the primary problem with table saw vibration is how it affects cutting performance. If you notice your saw vibrating more than normal, the two likely culprits to check are the belts and pulleys or the arbor and blade.

Tuning up motor & arbor drive pulleys

On contractor's and cabinet saws, the pulleys on the motor and arbor must line up with one another. Otherwise, the drive belt or belts will ride unevenly in the pulleys and set up vibration in the arbor assembly, which will transfer right into the blade. Also, the motor shaft and the arbor shaft must be parallel to one another to provide even tension on the belts.

Check pulley alignment by laying a straightedge against both the outer rim of the pulley on the arbor and the counterpart rim on the motor shaft. The straightedge should be flat against both rims. If it isn't, loosen the setscrew on the motor shaft pulley and slide the pulley in or out along the shaft until all the pulley rims line up. If you still can't get the pulley rims to align, the arbor and motor shafts are not parallel with one another. Adjust the shafts by loosening the bolts that hold the motor on the motor mounting plate and shift the motor slightly until the pulleys come into alignment. NOTE: *The mounting bolts should be outfitted with lockwashers underneath the nuts to keep them tight. Add lockwashers before you retighten the bolts, if your saw doesn't have them.*

Check the condition of the drive belt or belts on your saw while you are aligning the pulleys. The tapered inner surfaces of the belts should be smooth and free of splits or missing chunks of rubber. The belts should ride evenly on the pulleys, just below the top edges of the rims. If your belts look dried out, worn or damaged, or if they slap and vibrate when the saw is running, replace all of them at one time with the correct factory replacements recommended for your saw. Don't make the mistake of substituting automotive fan belts—they're engineered for different tolerances, speeds and pulley geometries.

Adjusting drive pulleys

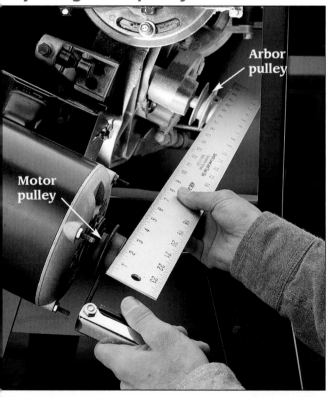

Shift the motor pulley. Set a straightedge against the rims of the motor and arbor pulleys to check their alignment. If the straightedge won't sit flat against both pulleys at the same time, loosen the screw that holds the motor pulley in place and slide it in or out on the motor shaft until the pulleys line up.

Shift the whole motor. If adjusting the motor pulley still doesn't line up the pulleys, loosen the motor mounting bolts and shift the motor to make up the difference. It may help to loosen up only three of the four mounting bolts and use the fourth bolt as a pivot point to keep the motor from moving too far.

Tips for reducing vibration

Check and replace drive belts. Dried out, worn or cracked drive belts contribute to saw vibration. Replace a worn drive belt with a matching belt designed specifically for your table saw.

Stabilize the rear trunnion. You may be able to reduce vibration emanating from the arbor and trunnions by fastening a C-clamp to the rear trunnion and the back of the cradle assembly.

Correct arbor & blade runout

If you've checked other possible sources of vibration and the saw still vibrates excessively, turn your attention to the blade and arbor. The arbor and blade must spin in the same flat plane for the blade to cut accurately. If either the blade or the arbor wobble out of the flat plane of rotation, the saw will vibrate. This wobbling is called *runout*.

Remove the saw blade from the arbor and inspect the arbor flange closely (See photo, left). It only takes a small amount of dirt, compacted sawdust or a burr on the metal to prevent the blade from butting tightly against the flange. Clean the flange with mineral spirits and a bristle brush first. Then slide your finger around the flange, feeling for imperfections. You are most likely to find nicks or burrs on the arbor when it is new. File off any nicks or burrs. Note: *Choose a fine-toothed flat file and remove as little metal as possible, to keep the flange face flat. You can also rub away irregularities with a fine-grit sharpening stone.*

While you inspect the flange, check the arbor for worn bearings, which can also lead to arbor runout. Remove the drive belt and spin the arbor. If you hear clicking or grinding, one or more arbor bearings are bad and should be replaced.

Reinstall the blade and see if the vibration disappears. If cleaning the arbor flange doesn't solve the problem, turn your attention to possible blade runout.

Cleaning a dirty arbor flange may be all it takes to eliminate excess vibration. The blade must sit flat against the rim of the arbor flange, or it will wobble and lead to more vibration. Use mineral spirits and a soft cloth to remove accumulated wood pitch or sawdust.

How to test for arbor & blade runout with a dial indicator

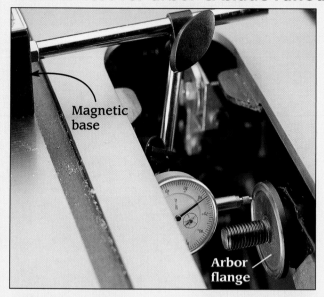

Magnetic base

Arbor flange

After you've cleaned the arbor flange, removed any burrs and tried several different blades in an attempt to reduce vibration, persistent vibration indicates that either the arbor or the blade have excessive runout. Use a *dial indicator* to measure the amount of runout on your arbor flange first, then test your blades. A dial indicator is a machinist's tool that measures the amount of deflection on a shaft or blade in thousandths of an inch.

To test for arbor flange runout, pick up a dial indicator that clamps to a magnetic base. Remove the saw blade. Set the dial indicator base on the saw table close to the blade. Adjust the apparatus so the contact point on the dial touches the flat face of the arbor flange. Set the dial to zero. Then, rotate the arbor shaft slowly by hand as you watch the dial. The overall amount of deflection from zero should not exceed .003. If it does, consider having the arbor and flange retrued by a machine shop or replacing the arbor altogether. Any more deflection than this will translate to rougher cuts on your workpieces.

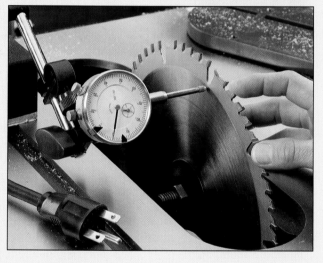

To test blade runout, mount the blade to the arbor and tighten the arbor nut. Set the dial indicator in position with the contact point against the blade as far out to the edge of the blade as possible. Keep the contact point far enough inset so it doesn't accidentally catch in the blade tooth gullets (the "valleys" between the teeth). Then, rotate the blade slowly. All blades will have some runout, and runout will slowly increase as the blade heats and cools repeatedly. Blade runout should not exceed .012 on 10-in. blades. If your blade does, it's time to buy a new blade.

If you've just installed a new or resharpened blade on your saw and notice more vibration, the problem is likely coming from the blade. The blade's arbor hole may be slightly off center or larger than the diameter of the arbor shaft, which will make the blade spin out of round on the arbor shaft. It's possible that if the blade was just sharpened or subjected to a trauma like overheating or kickback, the blade body may have fallen out of balance. Try a different blade in the saw to see if another blade remedies the problem. Shifting the blade to a new location on the arbor shaft may also improve runout, so loosen the arbor nut, rotate the blade a quarter turn on the arbor and retighten the nut. Or you could add a pair of blade stiffeners (See photo, right) to the blade, which sandwich the blade on one or both sides and stiffen the blade body.

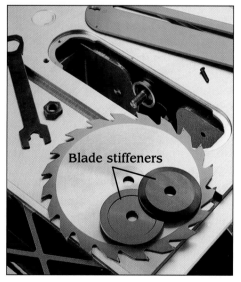

Blade stiffeners

Minor blade runout can be improved by installing metal blade stiffeners on each side of the blade. Stiffeners are sold in different diameters. Keep in mind that larger-diameter blade stiffeners will make contact with workpieces if the blade is raised too far.

Periodic cleaning & lubrication

A little routine maintenance goes a long way toward prolonging the life of your saw. In addition to regular tune-ups, your saw will benefit from regular cleaning and lubrication. Here are a few tips to follow.

Vacuum the saw base, internals & motor

Table saws create a tremendous amount of sawdust, and it will accumulate in a hurry unless you clean it up every time you are finished sawing. Sweep off the tabletop and wipe off the fence rails as you work to keep the rip fence and miter gauge sliding smoothly. After you finish cutting for the day, take time to brush out and vacuum inside the saw base (See photo, right), particularly around the motor's cooling vents and along the trunnions and arbor assembly where the worm gears engage.

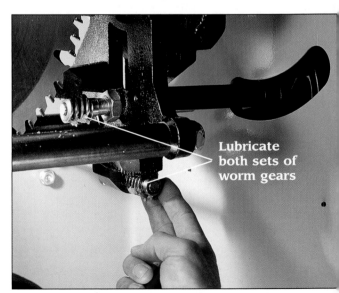

Clean & polish the saw table

Treat the metal tabletop (including the miter slots), fence rails and miter gauge with a coat of paste wax every month or so. This is especially important for cast-iron and exposed steel surfaces of the saw, which are prone to rust. Apply wax more frequently if your shop is in a damp basement or garage where the level of humidity is high. Waxing these parts not only will keep the bare metal from rusting but also will keep workpieces and saw parts sliding smoothly over the saw table. Choose a paste-style wax formulated for automobiles or furniture, but check the label to be sure the wax does not contain silicone. Silicone will absorb into your workpieces and repel wood finishes. Spread the wax evenly, rub it in and allow it to dry to a haze, then buff off excess wax with a soft towel.

Use a synthetic pad and naval jelly or automotive rubbing compound to remove minor rust and pitting when it occurs and mineral spirits to remove wood pitch. Follow these treatments immediately with a coat of wax.

Lubricate worm gears & moving parts

Eventually you'll have to remove gummed-up, dried sawdust and pitch deposits from the trunnions and worm gears, as well as other nooks and crannies inside the saw base and behind the blade. Resinous woods like pine and woods that aren't thoroughly dry will gunk up a saw even faster. Use a soft brass- or plastic-bristle brush and mineral spirits to soften and scrape away impacted sawdust. Once the parts are clean and dry, lubricate the worm and trunnion gears and other pivot points with powdered graphite, a non-silicone spray lubricant or a dab of paste wax. If you use graphite, keep it away from the saw table, or it will act like silicone on wood and repel wood finishes. Although you may be tempted to use it, steer clear of petroleum greases to lubricate your table saw. Grease will only attract and trap the grit and sawdust.

Lubricate both sets of worm gears

Clean & protect blades from rust

It's important to keep saw blades clean and rust-free. When pitch and gum deposits accumulate on the blade, the blade can't dissipate heat as effectively, so it heats up more quickly, which can cause cracks. Dirty, gummed-up blade teeth simply attract more pitch and gum, so the problem compounds over time. And some wood resins will eventually corrode carbide teeth. Accumulated wood pitch also affects the blade's balance as it spins.

Commercial blade cleaners do a fine job of removing blade deposits. However, you can save money by simply soaking the blade in spray-on oven cleaner for about an hour, then scrubbing the blade clean with a synthetic abrasive pad and a clean towel. Once the blade is clean, inspect it carefully under a bright light for cracks. Use a magnifying glass to examine the carbide teeth for chips, dulled edges or cracks in the brazing that hold the teeth to the blade. Then protect the blade from rust with a light coating of wax or oil.

Table Saw History

Double-blade flooring saw

Carroll's Patent Gang Saw, manufactured in the early 1870s, was designed to rip-cut 4- to 6-in.-wide planks for flooring. It featured two ripping blades on the arbor—the right blade fixed in place and the left blade adjustable to the right or left. By outfitting multiple blades on the arbor, the saw could rip up to three widths of flooring simultaneously from a single board—one plank between the rip fence and right blade, the second between the two blades and a third to the left of the left blade. A handle mounted on the front of the saw made adjustments to the left blade possible without wrenches, to economize set-up time.

This belt-driven saw was outfitted with a feed roller behind the blades to pull lumber through the blades. A published review of this machine estimated that it could saw between 10,000 and 12,000 board feet of flooring in a 10-hour workday, double the productivity of other flooring saws at the time.

Carroll's Patent Gang Saw (circa 1873)

Choosing Saw Blades

Tuning up your saw will dramatically improve the accuracy of your cuts, but don't overlook the importance of choosing the right blade for the job. At first glance, blades look basically the same, but that doesn't mean one blade will perform all cuts equally well. Differences in the shape and number of blade teeth distinguish blades meant for ripping, crosscutting, trimming laminates or cutting plywood. You won't need a drawer full of saw blades to be properly outfitted, but choosing a few blades carefully and using the right blade for the task will go a long way toward producing cuts that require little sanding or planing.

To make wise blade choices, you need to know a few details about blade anatomy and types of blades, as well as how to tell a quality blade from a poor one. The next few pages should provide all the information you'll need to buy a hardworking, comprehensive set of blades for your table saw.

Know the parts

A blade begins as a plate of steel that is stamped or laser cut to shape, forming the *blade body.* The steel is heat-treated to temper it to a certain hardness, then tensioned. *Tensioning* is a process of compressing a ring around the circumference of the blade body near the *rim* to help the blade dissipate stress and heat more efficiently so it doesn't warp. An *arbor hole* (usually undersized) is punched into the center of the blade body, then reamed wider to a precise diameter. The blade body is ground flat and, on most blades, uniformly thick. (Some blades with steel teeth, called *planer blades,* are "hollow-ground," so they are thicker near the center and ground thinner out to the teeth.) The *gullets* and *shoulders* are also ground smooth.

Located between the teeth, gullets serve a cooling function, like the thin fins on a radiator. But their

Anatomy of a blade

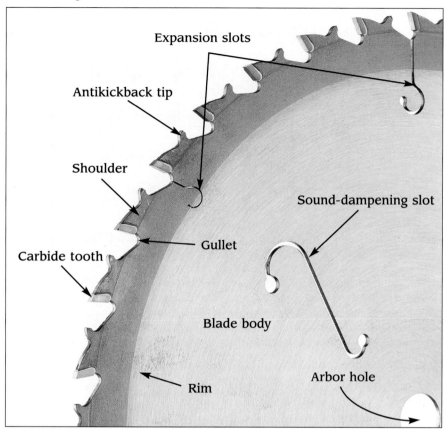

Saw blades are made in a variety of styles and tooth counts, each engineered for specific cutting tasks. Most saw blades feature carbide teeth, which hold an edge longer than steel teeth. Better-quality blades will have a number of expansion slots cut into the blade body to keep it from warping as it heats up. Some manufacturers also add sound-dampening slots to diffuse vibration that would create excessive blade noise.

Understanding hook angles

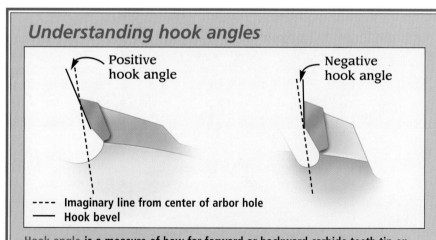

Hook angle is a measure of how far forward or backward carbide teeth tip on the blade shoulders. Blades have "positive" hook angles when the teeth tip forward and "negative" hook angles when teeth tip backward. The degree of hook is measured from an imaginary line (considered 0°) extending from the center of the blade arbor hole to the tip of the carbide tooth. Hook angles range from 20° (ripping blades) to -6° (laminate-cutting blades). Teeth with positive hook angles cut more quickly and produce larger chips than teeth with negative hook.

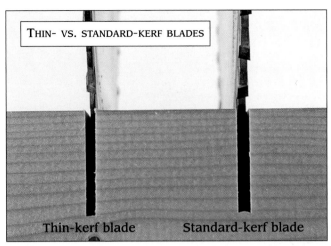

Thin-kerf blade   Standard-kerf blade

Thin-kerf saw blades are a relatively recent innovation in blade design. The usual kerf width for standard saw blades is about ⅛ to 3/16 in., but the thickness of a thin-kerf blade is closer to 3/32 in., so it removes less material when it cuts. The big advantage to using a thin-kerf blade is that you'll need less saw power to perform the same cut as a standard-kerf blade. Consider buying a thin-kerf blade if you own a saw with a motor less than 1½ h.p. The downside to thin-kerf blades is that they are more likely to deflect when cutting thick or dense woods.

Carbide teeth

Carbide teeth are incredibly hard, but they will dull and even chip as the teeth wear. Both of the blades shown here have alternate top bevel teeth, but notice the corroded, chipped and missing tips on the top blade compared with the new blade on the bottom. Carbide teeth can be resharpened several times on better blades, but the carbide teeth on the top blade should be replaced. Have your carbide-tipped blades serviced by a qualified saw sharpener, or send the blades back to the manufacturer for repairs.

main job is to evacuate chips and sawdust from the saw kerf. *Shoulders* reinforce the area behind each tooth. Some blades are designed with special *antikick-back tips* on the shoulders, to limit how deeply each tooth bites into the wood.

Better-quality saw blades commonly have several *expansion slots* cut down from the gullets and through the rim. As the blade heats up during a cut, the slots allow the blade to expand closer to the teeth instead of deeper in the body, which can cause warpage. Some blades also feature *sound-dampening slots* that absorb excess vibration so the blade cuts more smoothly and quietly.

The business end of any blade is its teeth. You'll find that *carbide teeth* have replaced steel teeth on virtually every saw blade made these days. This is because carbide, a mixture of tungsten carbide particles and a cobalt binder, holds an edge 40 to 50 times longer than steel teeth. The downside to carbide is that it is brittle, which means carbide teeth will chip or break if the teeth strike something harder than wood (See photo, bottom left). And unlike plain steel teeth, the complex tooth grinds found on many carbide teeth are almost impossible to sharpen yourself.

Carbide teeth are brazed into pockets in the blade shoulders, ground to the proper profile with diamond abrasives, then smoothed until the teeth are razor sharp. Depending on the blade, the shoulders will hold the carbide teeth so they pitch forward or backward, forming an angle relative to an imaginary line that extends from the center of the arbor hole. This angle, known as *hook,* is considered *positive* if the teeth pitch forward and *negative* if the teeth have no angle or tip backward on the shoulders (See *Illustration,* page 49). Blades made for rip-cutting have a positive hook angle, so the teeth remove larger chips and cut more quickly. Blades for cutting laminate and particleboard, on the other hand, have negative hook angles so the teeth scrape, rather than chip or shear what they cut. Negative-hook blades cut more slowly and produce smaller chips, but they leave glass-smooth cuts with minimal chipping and tearout.

Know the grinds

Carbide teeth are ground across the top in one of three ways: *flat, beveled* to the left or right, or *chamfered* on both tips. The type of grind affects how the teeth cut. By combining these three tooth grinds in different patterns, blades can be classified according to the following four grind configurations.

Flat top grind (FT)

FT grinds are used primarily on blades intended for rip-cutting. Each blade tooth is ground flat across the top, so it acts like a miniature chisel, chipping away material in the saw kerf. Blades with FT grinds typically have a positive hook angle of around 20° and deep gullets between the teeth.

Alternate Top Bevel (ATB)

ATB blade teeth bevel to the left and right in an alternating pattern. Rather than chip as they cut, the teeth shear wood like tiny knives. ATB blades are best suited for making smooth crosscuts, but they make adequate rip cuts as well. Bevel angles on ATB teeth will vary, ranging from 5° to 40°. Steeper, narrower bevels will cut more cleanly than shallower, shorter bevels, but the teeth will dull more quickly.

Alternate Top Bevel & Raker (ATB & R)

The teeth on ATB & R blades are configured into groups of two to four beveled teeth, followed by one raker tooth. Blades with this hybrid tooth design are commonly called *combination blades,* and they are designed to perform both rip-cutting and crosscutting functions. Combination blades are a good choice if you only buy one blade for your saw. They won't perform either rip cuts or crosscuts quite as well as blades designed only for these purposes, but combination blades will do a decent job with either cut. If you use only a combination blade, plan on smoothing your cut edges with a hand plane or on the jointer.

Triple-Chip Grind (TC)

Half of the teeth on TC ground blades are chamfered on both corners, and the other half are flat-top teeth. The chamfered teeth clear out most of the waste in the saw kerf, and the flat-top teeth clean up the corners. Most TC blades have a negative hook angle in order to make smooth cuts in composite materials like MDF, melamine and laminate. They can also cut plastic and non-ferrous metal.

Blade storage cabinet

Store your blades in a sturdy, accessible container, like the blade cabinet shown above. This simple design employs ¼-in. plywood dividers to form separate compartments for each blade. If you build a similar cabinet for your blades, keep the blades from rolling out by tipping the base backward slightly, and fasten a lip along the front edge.

Evaluating carbide-tooth blade quality

Here are a few pointers to keep in mind next time you are blade shopping for your table saw. Don't assume that you must buy the most expensive blades. If you are a general-purpose woodworker, buy blades that fall in the middle price ranges and have the following characteristics:

1 Blade bodies should have fine grind marks that radiate out in concentric rings toward the rim. Grinding shows that the blade was flattened, balanced and finished to a specific thickness. Hold a straightedge against the blade body and shine a light behind it. Only the slightest sliver of light (or none at all) should show between the straightedge and the blade.

2 The arbor hole should be free of burrs. Arbor holes on inferior blades are often punched but not reamed and ground smooth. Grinding ensures that the hole is centered and will fit the saw arbor exactly.

3 Inspect the brazing behind each tooth. Brazing should be ground smooth and reveal no pitting, burrs or gaps next to the teeth.

4 Examine the carbide teeth with a magnifying glass. They should be smooth, sharp and polished on all edges. Buy blades with the thickest carbide teeth you can find; thicker teeth can be sharpened more times before they must be replaced.

Common blade types

Should you decide to own only one blade, make it either a combination or crosscut-style. But eventually you'll want to broaden your inventory to include specialty blades. Each blade type shown here is designed to make specific kinds of cuts. Some can do double duty, but you'll get top results when you saw with the blade best suited for the task.

1. Combination blade

A true "jack-of-all trades" blade, combination blades make rip cuts and crosscuts equally well in all woods. Teeth are ATB & R grind, grouped in sets of two to four beveled teeth plus one raker. Deep gullets in front of the raker teeth remove chips quickly. Tooth counts range from 24 to 50 teeth for 10-in.-dia. blades.

2. Ripping blade

Ripping blades cut quickly and smoothly with the wood grain, which is why they have only 18 to 24 flat-top teeth and deep gullets. A ripping blade makes poor crosscuts. These blades work best when used with a saw that has at least 2 h.p.; their aggressive hook angle and wider teeth require plenty of sawing muscle.

3. Crosscut blade

Crosscut blades have higher tooth counts (up to 80 teeth on 10-in. blades) than either ripping or combination blades. Their shallow gullets and alternating beveled teeth produce smooth crosscuts with little or no tearout in hardwoods, softwoods and sheet goods. They are also make suitable, but slower, rip cuts.

4. Laminate-cutting blade

A good choice for cutting MDF, melamines, laminates and plastics, laminate blades combine triple-chip ground teeth plus flat-topped rakers, all set at a negative hook angle of up to -6°. These 40- to 80-tooth blades take small bites, so the cuts will be free from both tearout and chipping.

5. Plywood blade

An economical alternative to carbide-tipped crosscut and laminate blades, these blades use up to 200 tiny high-speed-steel teeth to make smooth cuts in plywood. Plywood blades require slow feed rates, and they'll dull much quicker than carbides, especially when used to cut particleboard. When the blade dulls, dispose of it.

Dado blades

Dado blades are modified saw blades designed to cut grooves up to 13⁄16 in. wide. A dado blade cuts only partway through a board (called *non-through cuts*) as opposed to cutting a board in two, (called *through cuts*). Dado blades are used mainly to cut interlocking parts for wood joints. For more on using dado blades for wood joinery, see pages 98 to 129. Incidentally, when a dado blade cuts along the grain of a workpiece, the groove is called a *plow,* while a *dado* is the proper term for cuts made across the grain.

Types of dado blades

Dado blades come in two forms: *stacked dado blades* and *wobble dadoes.* Stacked dado blades consist of a pair of carbide-tipped saw blades that sandwich one to five *chipper blades* in between. The teeth on these outside blades bevel outward, so they shear the walls of the dado and establish the width of the kerf. The chipper blades clean out the waste between the walls. Most chippers look more like lawnmower blades than saw blades, with one carbide tooth on each end of a rectangular blade body. Some dado-blade sets have cross-shaped chippers instead, with four teeth.

Stacked dado-blades are so named because the outer blades and chippers are stacked on the saw arbor in a configuration that matches the thickness of

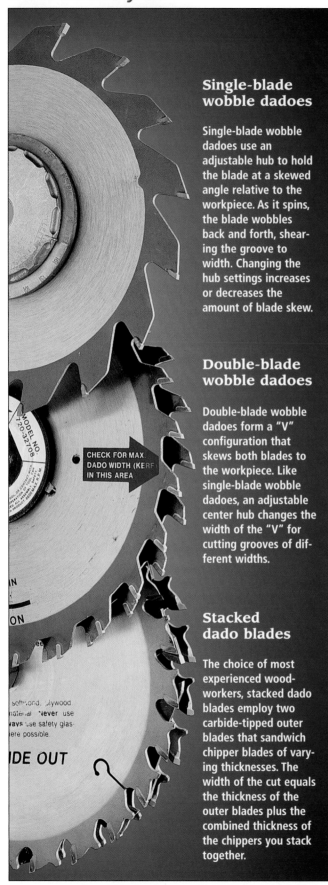

Single-blade wobble dadoes

Single-blade wobble dadoes use an adjustable hub to hold the blade at a skewed angle relative to the workpiece. As it spins, the blade wobbles back and forth, shearing the groove to width. Changing the hub settings increases or decreases the amount of blade skew.

Double-blade wobble dadoes

Double-blade wobble dadoes form a "V" configuration that skews both blades to the workpiece. Like single-blade wobble dadoes, an adjustable center hub changes the width of the "V" for cutting grooves of different widths.

Stacked dado blades

The choice of most experienced woodworkers, stacked dado blades employ two carbide-tipped outer blades that sandwich chipper blades of varying thicknesses. The width of the cut equals the thickness of the outer blades plus the combined thickness of the chippers you stack together.

When installing a stacked dado blade, **it's important to stack the blades together so the chipper teeth adjacent to the outer blades are positioned within the gullet areas of the outer blades (See inset photo). This way, the teeth will overlap across the kerf width and remove all of the waste in the cut. Arrange the chippers so that they radiate around the circumference of the outer blades to balance the blades on the arbor.**

Dialing in width settings on wobble dadoes

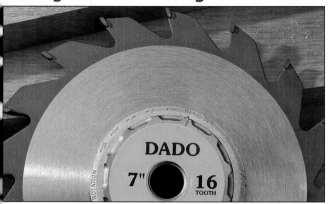

Single-blade wobble dadoes cut grooves of various widths by adjusting a center hub. The hub is marked for different cutting widths, but these are rough estimates at best. Make cuts on a scrap piece first to verify the blade setting.

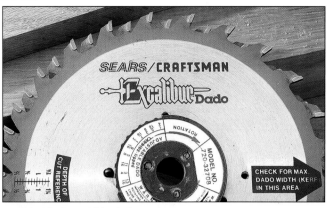

Double-blade wobble dadoes also are adjustable by twisting a center hub. Turning the hub changes the width of the "V" shape formed by the blades. The blade shown here also has references for determining blade height and actual cutting width.

the cut you need. The chippers vary in thickness, from 1/16 in. to 1/4 in. By switching the combination of chippers, stacked dado blades can cut dadoes or plows ranging from 1/4 in. to 13/16 in. in increments of 1/16 in. For instance, to cut a 7/16-in. groove, the stack could consist of the two outer saw blades, which typically have 1/8-in. kerfs, plus one 1/8-in. and one 1/16-in. chipper blade.

Wobble dadoes operate on a completely different principle than stacked dado blades. Instead of two outer blades and a series of chippers in between, most wobble dadoes are simply a bevel-toothed blade mounted on a wedge-shaped hub. As the dado spins, it wobbles back and forth on its axis, shearing away a swath of material across the width of the cut. The center hub is adjustable and marked for different kerf width settings. By turning the hub, you change the pitch of the blade on the saw arbor.

A second, less common wobble-dado style consists of two bevel-toothed blades that form a "V" configuration on the arbor. Like their single-blade cousins, two-blade wobble dadoes can be adjusted to cut dadoes of various widths by adjusting a wedge-shaped center hub. As you turn the hub, the distance between the blades at the top of the "V" narrows or widens.

Choosing a dado blade

Stacked dado blades are more expensive than either wobble-style, and the cost among stacked dado blades will vary. More teeth or chippers generally raises the price. Despite the cost, stacked dadoes tend to produce smoother cuts than either single- or double-blade wobble dadoes. A top-quality stacked dado will cut dadoes with flat, square walls, a flat bottom and minimal tearout on the surface of the workpiece. How well a stacked dado blade cuts will depend on how closely the diameter of the chippers matches the diameter of

the outside blades, as well as the sharpness of the blade teeth.

Wobble dadoes are the least expensive dado type, at about 1/4 to 1/2 the price of a stacked dado. Good-quality models can cut quite cleanly with minimal tearout. However, wobble dadoes produce cuts that slope at the bottom at most settings because the blade is cutting at an angle to the workpiece rather than straight on. The amount of slope will change as you adjust the wobble dado to different width settings. Double-blade wobble dadoes are capable of cutting dadoes that are closer to flat across the bottom, but most settings create bottoms that are "dished" in or out; a by-product of sawing with skewed blades.

An uneven-bottomed dado is fine if the bottom doesn't have to show, or if you clean up and square the bottom of the cut with a router or chisel afterward. If you plan to use a dado blade for "hogging" out material rather than for finer finished joint cutting, a wobble-style dado will suit you well.

Which size is right for your saw?

Both stacked and wobble-style dado blades are sold in 6-, 8-, and 10-in. diameters. Manufacturers recommend using a dado blade with a diameter 2 in. smaller than the maximum blade size for your saw. The smaller size recommendation is due to the fact that dado blades are heavy and create more stress on the saw arbor as they spin. Wobble-style dadoes produce considerable vibration as well, which must be soaked up by the saw, or they'll transfer into rough cuts. Be wary of using a dado blade on light-duty benchtop saws with motors rated at less than 1 1/2 h.p. Refer to your owner's manual to see if a dado blade is a suitable accessory for your saw.

Making Basic Cuts

Table saws are not difficult to use successfully and safely as long as you follow a few basic guidelines. First, you need to choose your lumber carefully. Wood continues to change shape long after it's cut from the tree, due to fluctuations in moisture content and other internal stresses in the wood. Evaluate the condition of each piece of wood you plan to cut before you cut it. You may need to correct for various kinds of wood defects with other tools like jointers or portable saws before it's suitable for the table saw.

Second, know exactly which kind of cut you are making and have a specific plan in mind. Table saws essentially cut wood in two ways: along the grain (called *ripping*) and across the grain (called *crosscutting*). The procedures for making these two kinds of cuts are quite different. Be clear about these differences and exercise safe technique.

Third, take into account the bulkiness and propor-tions of your workpieces so you can negotiate them safely across the saw table. Your goal is to maintain control over yourself, the workpiece and the saw at all times to avoid accidents and mistakes.

Turning on the saw and passing wood through the blade is actually the quickest step of the cutting process. Choosing and measuring up your stock, set-ting a fence, clamping or supporting your workpieces and reviewing a cut in your mind is most time-consuming, but these steps are all necessary parts of a process that will ensure accurate, safe sawing.

CAUTION: *Some of the photographs you'll see through-out this book show the blade guard and splitter removed. This was done to make the information in the photo-graphs easier to see. To prevent injury, use a working blade guard and a splitter with antikickback pawls when-ever the type of cut being made allows it.*

Before you start cutting

Cutting wood involves more than just tuning up a table saw and installing a sharp blade. You also need to start with sound lumber that can be made flat and square on at least one face and one edge or end. Chances are, most lumber that ends up in your shop is neither straight nor flat. It also may have a number of

Cutting boards is an activity that involves two main players: the lumber and the saw. Selecting good lumber or salvaging what you can from inferior boards is as important to your cutting successes as using a sharp blade on a well-tuned saw. Workpieces should be dry, free of serious defects and be flat and square to ensure accurate, safe results when you make your final cuts.

other natural defects that are undesirable or even unsafe if they should come in contact with the blade. The next few pages will outline a few important properties of wood you should know, identify lumber defects to look out for and then help you evaluate how to correct these problems to create the best possible workpieces for sawing.

Understanding wood movement

Since wood once served a structural purpose for the tree, it retains a certain amount of internal stress that may resist your efforts to machine it straight and flat. The wood may have held up a heavy branch or come from a part of the trunk that twisted or curved in some way. A single board may be cut from two different regions of the tree trunk, and both regions will influence how the board reacts when you cut it.

Wood also acts like a sponge to water. Until you apply a protective topcoat to slow down the rate of change, expect your lumber to expand when the humidity rises in damp summer months and contract when the air dries out in fall and winter. Expansion happens most noticeably across the width of a board, perpendicular to the grain direction. If a board doesn't absorb and release moisture evenly, it will begin to distort or even split in extreme cases. To keep your lumber as stable as possible, store it in a place where levels of humidity remain relatively constant. Keep as much of the surface area of each board exposed as you can by stacking boards with narrow wood spacers in between, to improve the airflow around each board.

Testing moisture content

Stock purchased at a lumberyard varies widely in moisture content. The amount of moisture a board contains will affect how well the board cuts as well as how true and flat it will stay once the cut is made. The wetter the lumber is, the more difficult it will be to cut and the more likely it will be to split or warp once it is cut.

The ideal moisture content for furniture lumber is around 8 to 10%. The only way you can accurately test for moisture content is to use a calibrated moisture meter, available through woodworking catalogs. Most meters have a pair of sharp probes that you press into the end or edge of a board. A readout scale on the meter tells you the moisture percentage. Moisture meters can be expensive, but you may want to invest in one if do fine furniture work and the humidity in your shop fluctuates widely. You'll also want to test lumber before buying it fresh-sawn from a mill.

It's best to set aside lumber with a moisture content over 12% and allow it to air dry before you cut it. Retest moisture levels every couple of weeks.

A moisture meter will tell you immediately the moisture content of a board. The red glowing light on this meter indicates the moisture content in this board to be 10%, an acceptable level for cutting and for project use.

Identifying & evaluating wood defects

In any stack of lumber, you'll find four kinds of natural distortion occurring: twisting, bowing, crooking and cupping (See below). If a board's distortions are slight enough that you can't detect them at first glance, you can probably flatten and square it fairly easily using the techniques outlined on the next two pages. However, it may be impossible to salvage much worthwhile wood from severely distorted lumber. Keep in mind that even if you correct one or another kind of distortion, it could re-emerge over time. Evaluate how important a piece of distorted wood is to your project. You may want to discard it for a more suitable piece instead.

Other wood defects to identify are *checks* (cracks that usually begin on the ends of boards), *loose knots, pockets of sap, spalling* or *tunnels* left by wood-boring insects. You may even find boards with bark still attached (called *wane*), if you buy your lumber directly from the sawmill. It's impossible to avoid all lumber with defects, and some, like tight-grained knots, can even be desirable. Generally however, you should cut off these problem areas first to start with the most sound workpieces you can.

Spalling is a gray to green permanent discoloration of the wood caused by fungal growth.

Knots should be avoided when purchasing hardwoods, but in some cases you may be able to work around them.

Checking is a splitting of the wood grain at the end of the board. It can be cut off, but it may indicate that the board was not cured properly. If so, the board may actually begin to split again.

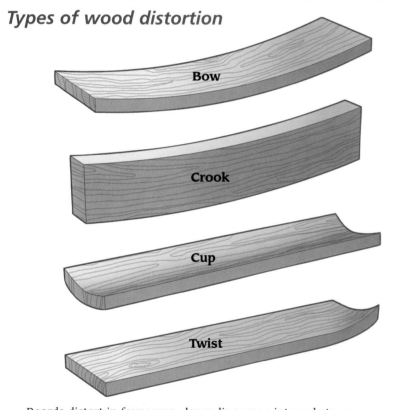

Types of wood distortion

Bow

Crook

Cup

Twist

Boards distort in four ways, depending upon internal stresses as well as how the board absorbs and releases moisture. Wood that **bows** is flat across its width but the faces curve lengthwise. A **crooked** board is flat across the face but curves along the edges in one direction or the other, like the rocker on a rocking chair. **Cupping** is occurring when a board is flat along its edges but curls across its width. **Twist** is the condition where one or more corners of a board turn up or down when you lay the board on a flat surface. It's fairly common to find a couple of these distortions happening in the same board. The more pronounced the distortions are in a board, the harder it will be to salvage much useful lumber.

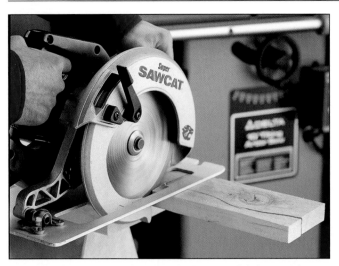

Trim off split ends, loose knots and other wood defects with a portable saw before cutting a problem board on the table saw.

Salvaging lumber

In many instances, you can salvage distorted or defective lumber by cutting, jointing and planing problem areas away, creating smaller pieces of lumber with flat faces and edges. Generally, the easiest and safest way to cut down irregular boards is to use a portable circular saw, jig saw or hand saw (See photo, top). The small base of a portable saw can follow the irregularities of a twisted board far better than a large, flat table saw table can. Use the portable saw as a resizing tool, then cut your finished edges on the table saw.

If you choose to cut defective lumber down first on the table saw, start with at least one flat edge for guiding against the rip fence or with the miter gauge. Flat-ten the edge with a hand plane or on a power jointer. If you don't own a jointer, you can flatten the edges of a crooked or waney board on your table saw by overlapping one undesirable edge with another board that has a flat edge. Fasten the boards together with finish nails or small screws. Run the flat edge of the tacked-on board against the saw fence to trim off the opposite, rough edge on the defective workpiece (See photo, bottom left). Separate the boards and run the cut edge of the workpiece against the rip fence to square the board.

When cutting bowed lumber on the table saw, set the flatter face down to minimize rocking as you cut. If a board is cupped, it's best to make rip cuts with the concave side facing up (See photo, bottom right). Ripping with the convex side facing up will cause the board to flatten out against the blade as the cut progresses, which could bind the wood between the fence and blade and cause it to kick back. If the board is sufficiently thick, you also may be able to correct for cupping by knocking off high areas first with a hand plane or on the jointer to flatten it, then running the board through a surface planer to smooth the faces. Simply running a cupped board through a planer won't eliminate cupping. A planer will temporarily flatten the board as it passes through the feed rollers, but it cannot remove the curling stresses present in the wood.

As far as other imperfections are concerned, cut off areas with loose knots, splits or spalling. Cut well around soft pockets of sap to keep from gumming up your blade. If you are using wood recycled from other projects, always inspect carefully for nails, staples or other construction debris before you saw. Hitting a metal fastener will invariably damage your saw blade.

Flatten the edges of crooked lumber or remove bark-covered (waney) edges by attaching a flat scrap over one rough edge. Run the flat edge against the rip fence. Then, remove the flat scrap and flip the board around to cut the other edge flat.

Cut cupped lumber with the concave side facing up. In severe cupping situations, as with this board, saw the board into smaller flat pieces. Keep the board from rocking as you cut it, to reduce the chances of kickback.

Procedure for squaring up stock

Flatten and smooth board faces. Once you've cut away defective areas and flattened high spots with a hand plane or jointer, smooth both board faces by running it through a surface planer, alternating the board faces with each pass.

Flatten one edge of your stock with a planed face against the jointer fence. Then guide this flat edge against the rip fence on the table saw to cut the board to width. Joint this cut edge smooth, if necessary, to remove saw marks.

Setting up for the cut

Before cutting a board you'll need to make some decisions about how to set up the table saw and related safety equipment to accomplish your task most effectively and safely. Ultimately, your goal should be to keep your motions fluid and controlled as you push wood through the saw blade. Fluid, steady motions will produce smooth, accurate cuts and minimize your chances for injury. It will also make cutting wood an enjoyable part of woodworking. To this end, here are a few suggestions to follow as you prepare for any cut:

1. Start with flat, square stock that is free from defects and is reasonably dry. (See the above photos for more information on squaring up stock.)

2. Give yourself plenty of room around the saw. Route the power cord so it won't pose a tripping hazard. Allow yourself 4 to 6 ft. of room to the left and to the right of the extension wings and 8 to 10 ft. in front of and behind the saw. The amount of clear space you'll need will vary, depending upon the dimensions of the workpiece you're cutting and whether or not you'll be using extra outfeed support devices as you cut. The goal here is to create a workspace that allows you to keep your attention focused entirely on what's going on at the saw table, not on the side stepping you might need to do to get around the pile of scraps you didn't clear off the floor from the last few cuts. Nothing should break your concentration or obstruct the path of your workpiece while you are making a cut.

Keep the sawing area clear

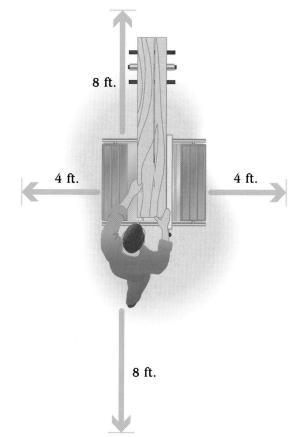

Make room for sawing. Allow 4 ft. of clear space on each side of the saw and 8 to 10 ft. in front and in back so you'll have plenty of room to work.

3. Choose the right blade for the material you are cutting.
Refer to the chapter on "Choosing Saw Blades," pages 48 to 55, to match your cutting tasks with the proper blade.

4. Be sure the saw guard is in place and the splitter is aligned squarely behind the blade. For more on adjusting the splitter, see page 42.

CAUTION:
Some of the photographs you'll see throughout this book show the blade guard and splitter removed. This was done to make the information in the photographs easier to see. To prevent injury, use a working blade guard and a splitter with antikickback pawls whenever the type of cut being made allows it.

5. Clamp featherboards to the saw table when necessary.
Featherboards should be positioned just in front of the blade to guide the workpiece into the blade without binding against it. Never use featherboards or hold-downs on the outfeed (back) side of the blade when you are cutting a board into two pieces. Doing this could close up the saw kerf behind the blade and invite kickback. Set up your featherboards so the workpiece slides smoothly beside or beneath the featherboard without dragging or binding, but the featherboard keeps the board from backing out of the cut when you pull on the board (See next page for an example of proper featherboard set-up).

Setting blade height for making through cuts

When the blade is set low, so that only the tips of the teeth protrude above the board, all of the blade teeth above the saw table remain in the workpiece during the cut. With more teeth in the board, the blade develops more heat, which results in burned edges and, some will argue, an increased risk for kickback.

With the blade raised to full height, only a few teeth contact the workpiece at the front and back of the blade, resulting in a much cooler, and generally cleaner, cut. However, you are at greatest risk of blade exposure, especially if you saw without a guard.

Gullet

The best compromise between clean cuts and minimal blade exposure is to set the blade just high enough so the gullets between the teeth clear the top of the board (about ¼ to ⅜ in. on most blades).

6. Set the blade height to produce the smoothest cut possible without compromising your safety. The ideal blade height is a matter of debate among professional woodworkers. The safest blade is one with a minimal number of teeth protruding above the workpiece (about ⅛ to ¼ in exposure). However, low blade height means more teeth remain in the cut for longer periods of time, which leads to more friction in the saw kerf, resulting in burn marks on cut edges. As you crank the blade higher, notice that fewer teeth on the front and back edge of the blade are actually in the cut, which means the blade will heat up less and produce a smoother cut, but your risk of getting cut increases. Experiment with different blade height settings to see which works best for your work and gives you the most peace of mind.

If higher blade settings make you nervous, saw at a lower blade height, cutting just outside of your layout line. Then run the sawn edge over a jointer to remove any saw marks that a lower blade might leave on the workpiece. This way, you'll have the best of both worlds in the end—a safer blade setting for sawing and enough of a waste edge to joint smooth.

Use featherboards on top of or beside a workpiece to hold it securely against the saw table and the fence. Featherboards are designed to flex with the direction of feed but bind against the workpiece if the blade should attempt to force it backward and out of the cut. Install featherboards on the infeed side of the blade when you are cutting a workpiece in two.

7. Keep a pushstick within arm's reach at all times. Use a pushstick to guide the workpiece whenever your hands come within 6 in. of the blade. If you'll be ripping narrow stock between the blade and the rip fence, be sure to choose a pushstick narrow enough to fit between the blade and the workpiece.

8. Set up outfeed support for long workpieces. When making long rip cuts, you'll need a roller stand or worktable set up behind the saw to support the workpiece and waste piece as they exit the back of the saw. For long crosscuts, set up workpiece support alongside the saw, just beyond the left or right extension wing. Be sure the height for outfeed support stands is even with or slightly below the surface of the saw table so workpieces won't hang up on them during a cut. There are many different aftermarket outfeed support options available, including outfeed and extension tables that attach directly to the saw. You can also make your own (See pages 154 to 155).

Whichever outfeed device you choose, it should have a wide, firm stance on the floor so it will be stable in all directions and not prone to tip or shift away from the saw as you cut. You could also use a helper to support workpieces as they leave the saw (See page 92).

Making blade changes

Installing a saw blade is a simple operation, and you'll do it many times, especially if you use the same saw for all your cutting operations. First, unplug the saw. Remove the throatplate and raise the blade to its full height. Wedge a piece of scrap wood into one of the blade gullets to keep the blade from turning as you loosen the arbor nut. Examine the threads on the arbor to see whether they are cut clockwise or counterclockwise on the arbor, then use either the arbor nut wrench that came with the saw or an adjustable wrench to loosen the arbor nut. (Most table saws have left-handed threads on the arbor, so you'll turn the arbor nut clockwise to loosen it.) Remove the nut—be careful not to drop it into the saw base or onto the floor. Pull the arbor washer off and, with two hands, slide the blade off the arbor. Store the blade in a dry place with its teeth protected. Install a blade by reversing the removal procedure, but be sure to clean any sawdust deposits off the arbor flange and threads first. Tighten the nut firmly, but not so tight that it makes removal difficult later. Reinstall the throatplate and adjust it so it sits flush with the surface of the saw table.

Arbor nut

Arbor nut wrench

Provide a stable outfeed surface to support your workpiece when it extends over the side or back of the saw. Plans for building this handy outfeed table are found on pages 154 to 155.

Roller stands are another option for outfeed support. Workpieces glide over ball bearings on the one shown here. TIP: *Anchor the base with a weight to keep it from shifting.*

Table Saw History

Self-feeding ripping saw

This saw, manufactured in 1902, served as a production ripping saw for planing mills, furniture, wheel, wagon, buggy and piano factories, car, railway and locomotive shops, navy yards and arsenals. As shown in this engraving, the saw could be outfitted with a belt-driven, two-speed self-feeding attachment, which used a toothed disk in front of the blade and either a smooth or fluted roller on the outfeed side.

Built mostly of cast-iron, the saw featured a patented saw table that raised and lowered on a pair of screw gears to change blade height, rather than tilting the saw arbor. The 1⅜-in.-dia. steel blade arbor could accept one or multiple saw blades up to 22 in. in diameter. Driven by a centralized belt system in the factory, the arbor spun at 2,400 revolutions per minute, about half the speed of table saws built today. Notice the long rip fence and the fence scale mounted above the fence on the right side of the saw.

J. A. Fay & Co. No. 2½ Self-Feeding Ripping Saw (circa 1902)

Making the cut

Rip cuts

To *rip-cut* (or *rip*) a board means to cut it lengthwise, following the direction of the grain. Of the basic saw cuts you can make on the table saw, you'll probably spend more time ripping workpieces than performing any other kind of cut. This is because the table saw, with its self-aligning rip fence, is an exceptional tool for making rapid, smooth rip cuts.

Rip cuts can be made with portable saws, but the process is more time-consuming. It's also tricky to rip-cut accurately unless you have a steady hand to guide the saw or clamp a straightedge to your work. You'll need to set up workhorses or clamp your workpiece to a workbench—a task you won't need to do with a table saw.

Table saws, on the other hand, use the rip fence as a guide for rip-cutting, so the accuracy of the cut doesn't depend on how steadily you can hold and maneuver the saw along your layout line. Success of the cut, however, will still depend on how smoothly you guide the workpiece through the blade.

Rip cuts. When you cut a board along the grain, you are making a rip cut. You'll likely make more rip cuts than any other kind of cut on a table saw.

Setting the rip fence. To make accurate and safe rip cuts, the rip fence must be parallel to the blade (See *"Understanding blade heel,"* page 36). Begin setting up for the cut by sliding the fence along the fence rail until its distance from the blade roughly matches the width of the board you need to cut. Under most circumstances, the finished workpiece is cut from the portion of the board between the rip fence and the blade, and the waste piece is the section that falls away from the blade on the other side when you finish your cut.

With the saw unplugged, use a tape measure or rule to set the exact distance you need between the fence and the blade. Do this by measuring from the inside edge of a blade tooth (the tooth edge that faces the rip fence) to the face of the fence. Tap the fence into place. Don't make the mistake of measuring from the "outside" edge of a tooth, or your finished workpiece will be too narrow. Lock the fence into position and check the width setting again, to be sure the distance hasn't changed.

Raise the blade to a height sufficient to cut through

To set the rip fence, measure from the fence to the closest edge of the blade. This distance should match the exact width of the workpiece you need. For instance, the set-up in this photo will cut a workpiece that is 2½ in. wide.

Squaring the rip fence

If your rip fence tends to shift out of parallel **when you lock it down, which happens with many rip fences, try this simple tip: Before you lock the fence, press your palm against the center of the fence body that rides along the front fence rail to square the fence on the fence rail, then lock down the fence.**

Safe hand zones for rip cuts

Right hand zone

Left hand zone

6 in. 6 in.

Hand zones. **With the rip fence positioned to the right of the blade, your right hand zone extends across the depth of the saw table for pushing workpieces completely past the blade. Your left hand holds workpieces in place against the table as soon as they are cut free, so there's no need to extend it past the infeed edge of the blade. Neither hand should come within 6 in. of the blade. Always use pushsticks instead when you are this close to the blade.**

the workpiece in one pass. How much higher than the workpiece you set the blade is a judgment call that depends on your own comfort level. (See page 62 to learn more about the pros and cons of high versus low blade settings.) If you need to rip stock thicker than the maximum blade height of your saw, see *"Ripping thick boards,"* page 73.

Start the cut. Typically rip cutting is done with the fence on the right-hand side of the blade. In these situations, stand in front of the saw to the left of the blade with your left foot touching the left corner or leg of the saw base. The closer your body is to the saw, the less you'll need to reach over the blade as you complete the rip cut, which will help you maintain your center of balance throughout the process. If your workpiece is short enough, rest your waist against the front fence rail for added support. Stand far enough to the left of the blade so your waist clears the width of the workpiece. This way, if the saw should kick the workpiece back out of the blade, it is less likely to strike your body. However, stand as close as you can to the side of the workpiece so your right arm is aligned with the fence and the blade as you make the cut.

Start the saw. Set the workpiece against the rip fence, a couple inches in front of the blade. Wrap your right hand around the back end of the board. Use your left hand like a featherboard, holding it against the inside edge of the workpiece to snug it up against the fence. Slide the board ahead slowly with your right hand until the blade engages the workpiece, keeping your left hand well in front of the blade. Feed the stock into the blade smoothly and at a steady rate. You can judge your *feed rate* by the sound of the motor as you cut; try to keep the motor cutting at an even pitch. You'll gain a "feeling" for the appropriate feed rate the more you use your saw. Slow down your feed rate if the motor begins to bog down, especially when cutting particularly hard, wet or thick workpieces.

As you cut, apply three forces simultaneously to the workpiece—forward pressure with your right hand to feed the work, and downward and side pressure with your left hand to keep the workpiece flat on the table and snug against the fence. Watch the workpiece to make sure it is making contact with the rip fence. At no time should the workpiece stray away from the fence. It's natural to want to glance at the blade while you cut, but avoid the temptation—it won't tell you much about how the cut is progressing anyway.

Finish the cut. Keep the workpiece moving steadily through the entire cut. Continue pushing the workpiece into the blade with your right hand until the back end approaches the front of the saw table. For workpieces wider than 6 in., use your right hand to continue guiding the board through the blade. If the workpiece is less than 6 in. wide, use a pushstick instead of your right hand. Guide the board with your left hand and reach for a pushstick with your right. Position the pushstick securely over the end of the board, and use it to continue pushing the workpiece past the blade.

When the blade finally separates the board in two, hold the waste clear of the blade with your left hand or a second pushstick while you feed the other part of the workpiece clear past the blade with your right hand/pushstick. Then, clear the waste piece off the saw table by sliding it away from the blade with your left hand or a pushstick.

How to make a standard rip cut

1 Start rip cuts with your left foot against the front left corner of the saw base. Feed the workpiece with your right hand, and use your left hand to keep the workpiece snug against the rip fence. Have a pushstick handy whenever a workpiece requires your hand to be closer than 6 in. to the blade.

2 Continue feeding the workpiece through the blade with your right hand as the end of the board approaches the front edge of the saw table. Switch to a pushstick in your right hand if necessary. Keep your left hand on the infeed side of the blade at all times (See *Illustration,* previous page).

3 When the blade cuts the board in two, push the workpiece past the blade with your right hand until it clears the blade on the outfeed side. Slide the cutoff piece away from the blade with your left hand or a pushstick to prevent it from coming in contact with the blade.

Troubleshooting chart for rip cuts

Problem: Workpiece stops on the saw while making a cut

Possible causes: Typically a workpiece will hang up in a cut because the splitter is not in line with the blade, so the splitter catches the leading edge of the board. If your workpiece is thick, the board may be hitting the mounting posts that hold the guard to the splitter. Or the workpiece may be catching on the back edge of the throatplate.

Solutions: Inspect and realign the guard and splitter (See page 42). Adjust the throatplate (See page 33).

Problem: Workpiece veers away from the fence during a cut

Possible causes: Workpiece edges could be crooked (See page 59). Or, you could be steering the board with your right hand rather than just pushing it as you make the cut.

Solutions: Always work with flat, square stock. Install a featherboard and try another cut. If the problem persists, the blade is likely heeling on the outfeed side. Align the blade with the miter slots (See pages 36 to 37).

Problem: Workpiece begins to smoke during a cut

Possible causes: Wood can burn for a variety of reasons as you saw. Investigate these possible culprits: Is your blade dirty or dull? Is the saw kerf closing up around the blade on the outfeed side? Is your rip fence parallel to the blade?

Solutions: Clean your blade (See page 47). Install a splitter if you aren't already using one to keep the saw kerf open behind the blade. Adjust the rip fence so it is parallel to the miter slots and blade (See page 40).

Problem: Blade slows or stops during a cut

Possible causes: Stalling usually indicates that the saw kerf is closing up or you are sawing with a dirty or dull blade. If you are using a small saw to cut thick hardwood or wet or particularly resinous wood like fir, the wood may simply be taxing the limits or your saw. If you are using an extension cord, feel it. A warm cord or plug indicates that you may be using an undersized cord, and the motor is starving for power under load.

Solutions: Be sure to use a splitter. Slow down your feed rate as you push wood through the blade to give the saw more time to cut and the blade to evacuate chips from the kerf. Clean your blade and/or have it professionally sharpened. Or you may want to switch to a thin-kerf blade if you have a small saw (See page 50). Use the proper gauge extension cord to power your saw (See page 25).

Problem: Workpiece lifts off the saw table near the back of the blade during a cut

Possible causes: The workpiece could be bowing (See page 59). Or the kerf could be closing up behind the blade, and the blade is actually lifting the workpiece off the saw table. If you are using a featherboard, check to see that the clamps haven't shifted out of place or loosened their grip on the workpiece.

Solutions: Inspect your workpiece by sighting down its length to see if it is bowing. Check your rip fence's alignment to the blade to be sure the blade isn't heeling (See page 36). Tighten the clamps that hold the featherboard in position, if you are using one. In any case, it is imperative that workpieces stay snug against the saw table during a cut to avoid kickback.

Ripping long boards

When rip-cutting boards that are longer than about 4 ft., you won't be able to begin the cut with your body next to the saw table. In these cases, first set up an outfeed support device behind the saw.

Rest the front end of the board on the front edge of the saw table. Start the saw, move to the back of the board on the left-hand side and tilt it up, using the right- and left-hand positions for normal ripping. To start the rip, you'll want to keep the front edge of the board flat on the table as the blade engages it. However, this can be difficult to do when you're standing a few feet back from the saw. To compensate, lift the back edge of the board higher than the saw table to plant the front edge of the board firmly against the table. Then begin the cut, lowering the board so it rests on the saw table and walking with the board as you feed it through the blade with your right hand. Keep your eyes on the fence, and apply diagonal pressure with your left hand so the board stays snug with

When ripping long boards, tip the back edge of the board up so it is slightly higher than the saw table. Doing this will press the leading edge of the board firmly down on the saw table. Lower the back edge of the board as the cut progresses.

the fence. It will be trickier to keep long stock against the fence, so slow down your feed rate if necessary and make minor body position adjustments the minute you see any gap developing between the

fence and the workpiece. Once you reach the saw table, position your left foot against the left corner of the saw base and use pushsticks as necessary to complete the cut and clear away the waste piece.

Ripping short boards

Ripping short boards (less than 10 in. or so in length) can be hazardous, because you'll need to feed and support the workpiece close to the blade from start to finish. It can be tricky or impossible to work pushsticks close enough in to the blade guard to guide the workpiece, so you may be inclined to remove the guard altogether, which will make short rips even more dangerous. What's more, if your workpiece isn't longer than the blade, you'll complete the cut before the leading edge of the workpiece is even past the blade, which renders the splitter useless. The best option is to try to make your rip cut from a longer piece of stock, then crosscut the shorter length you need from the longer stock. This way you'll maintain full control over the workpiece without compromising your safety.

The safest technique for ripping short boards is to guide them in a crosscut sled rather than sliding them along the saw table against the rip fence. Be sure the crosscut sled you use is equipped with a blade guard. For more on crosscut sleds, see page 85.

When rip-cutting a single narrow workpiece **from a wider board, the narrow strip should be on the opposite side of the blade from the rip fence. With this setup, you'll keep the wider portion of the board between the blade and the rip fence to allow more room for your hand or a pushstick.**

At times, ripping short lengths of stock is unavoidable. In these circumstances, the safest course of action is to make the rip cut with a short workpiece immobilized in a crosscut sled (See photo, previous page). The advantage to using a sled in this situation is that you can hold the workpiece steady instead of having to slide it along the saw table against the fence. Be sure to hold the workpiece securely in the sled as you make the cut. Use a push pad or pushstick as a hold-down if necessary, especially if your crosscut sled has no blade guard.

Ripping narrow workpieces

Many woodworking projects will require you to rip strips of narrow stock into parts such as glass retainer strips, filler pieces or trim molding. If you have only one part to make, adjust the rip fence so the finished workpiece is actually the part that falls away from the blade when you complete the cut. This way, you'll keep the wider part of the stock between the rip fence and the blade, which is safer for your hands and a steadier means of guiding the workpiece than using a narrow pushstick.

If you need to rip a number of identical strips of narrow stock, the procedure to use will depend on how wide the final workpieces need to be. If you can set the fence far enough from the blade to fit a pushstick in between, then set up your rip cuts so the "inside" piece

Options for making narrow repetitive rip cuts

To rip a series of narrow workpieces, **set the distance between the blade and the rip fence to match the intended width of the workpieces you need. Use a narrow pushstick to guide the pieces along the rip fence and past the blade.**

Notch runs full length of jig →

Another option for ripping narrow strips **is to use a jig with a notched cutout to support the workpiece. The notched area of the jig should match the width of the workpieces you are ripping. Support the outside edge of the workpiece as you cut.**

(the part between the blade and rip fence) matches the width of the pieces you need to make. The "waste" piece will constitute the remainder of the stock you're ripping from on the other side of the blade. Use a narrow pushstick to guide workpieces through the blade (See bottom left photo, previous page).

The procedure changes if your strips are so narrow that the space between the rip fence and the blade guard doesn't leave enough room for the width of a narrow pushstick. In these cases, narrow rip cuts are still possible, but you'll have to build a simple jig with a notched cutout that matches the width of the strips you need (See bottom right photo, previous page). The width of the jig isn't important, so long as it is wide enough to give you room between the fence and the blade to safely negotiate your hand or a pushstick.

To set up the cuts, rest the jig against the rip fence so the notched side faces the blade, and adjust the rip fence until the blade touches the outside edge of the jig's notch. The blade will cut flush against the notch without cutting it off. Set your workpiece in the notch and make your rip cuts, supporting the outside corner of the workpiece closer to you with your left hand or a pushstick. As the workpiece narrows, use a pushstick in your left hand to keep your hand a safe distance from the blade.

Support long, narrow rip cuts as they leave the saw table just as you would for wider, heavier workpieces. Otherwise, workpieces will tend to tip up and off the back of the saw table as soon as the board is cut in two.

Understanding & preventing kickback

Kickback. A split second is all the time it takes for a saw blade to grab hold of a workpiece and throw it back in the direction of the saw operator. Protect yourself from kickback situations by sawing with a splitter in place, equipped with antikickback pawls. Stand clear of the workpiece's path behind the saw as you are cutting.

Kickback occurs when the saw blade grabs a workpiece and propels it straight back toward the saw operator. Typically kickback happens because the workpiece binds on the outfeed (back) side of the blade, pinching the blade enough for the saw teeth to grab hold and lift the board off the saw table. A saw can eject a board in a number of cutting situations, whenever the teeth have the opportunity to grab hold of a board. However, kickbacks are most likely to happen when making rip cuts without a splitter installed on the saw. You'll have no time to react when kickback happens, which is why splitters are so essential to making safe rip cuts. Never make rip cuts with the splitter removed. Stand clear of the path of your workpiece as you are making a rip cut, to keep the board from striking your body, should kickback occur.

Using a partial rip fence

It isn't always necessary or even a good idea to make rip cuts against a fence that extends from the front to the back of the saw table. When you are rip-cutting wet, green or wavy-grained wood, the saw kerf has a tendency to open up as the workpiece leaves the blade area. If it does, a full-length rip fence can actually force the spreading workpiece back against the side of the blade, which will lead to burned edges and can result in kickback. With the exception of large sheet stock, which requires a longer bearing surface, work-pieces really only need to be guided by the rip fence until they contact the blade. Some European table saws don't even come with a full-length rip fence.

To avoid the problem that can be caused by a spreading saw kerf, attach a shop-made *partial fence* (also called a *half* or *short fence*) to your rip fence. The partial fence should be made from a piece of dimen-sionally stable hardwood or sheet stock about 2 ft. long. Rout a ⅝-in.-wide slot about 18 in. long and ¼ in. deep along the center of the partial fence. This slot will form a recess for the heads of two countersunk car-riage bolts.

Rout a ⁵⁄₁₆-in.-wide slot inside the first slot that pen-etrates all the way through the thickness of the partial fence. The purpose of this slot is to make room for the carriage bolt shafts and allows you adjust the partial fence forward or backward along the rip fence.

Mount the partial fence to your rip fence with two ¼-in. carriage bolts, nuts and washers. You may have to drill guide holes through your metal rip fence if the fence doesn't have holes already drilled for attaching auxiliary fences.

Setting the partial fence

Set the partial fence so the end closer to the blade extends about 1 in. past the blade teeth on the infeed side. Adjust the position of the partial fence whenever you raise and lower the blade, since the location of the infeed blade edge changes as you change blade height.

Build a partial fence from a length of flat, square hardwood or sheet stock. Rout a pair of grooves one inside the other length-wise along the partial fence, and attach the partial fence to the rip fence with ¼-in. countersunk carriage bolts. The slots allow you to reposition the partial fence forward or backward along the rip fence as needed.

Partial fence

Clear space

The purpose of a partial fence is to provide clear space between the blade and the rip fence on the outfeed side of the blade. In cases where the saw kerf is likely to spread apart from internal stresses in the board, a partial fence will keep the workpiece from binding against the blade.

1 in. past front of blade

A partial fence should extend from the front edge of the rip fence to about 1 in. past the infeed edge of the blade.

Overarm blade guard

1 To rip stock thicker than the maximum blade height of your saw, make the first cut with the blade set to full height. Because a standard blade guard/splitter can't be used to make this cut, consider outfitting your saw with an overarm-style blade guard, as seen above.

2 Once you've completed the first rip cut, flip the workpiece end-for-end. Lower the blade so it is just high enough to finish the cut. Make the second pass. For both steps of this technique, you'll likely have to slow down your feed rate to keep the saw from bogging down in the cut.

Ripping thick boards

Boards that are more than about 3½ in. thick cannot be rip-cut in a single pass on most 10-in. saws. That's why most woodworkers prefer to rip thick lumber on the band saw rather than the table saw. Band saws have much thinner blades, so they create less friction and heat in the cut. Plus, band saws offer a much greater depth of cut (10 in. or more on most 14-in. band saws) than table saws.

If you don't own a band saw, you can rip thick boards on your table saw, but the procedure will require you to make two passes to complete the cut. Also, you'll have to remove the splitter if the splitter has antikickback pawls that would interfere with the cut. Standard guards and splitters come as a one-piece assembly, so you'll have to remove both the guard and the splitter, which leaves you vulnerable to both kickback and blade exposure.

The safest saws for ripping thick boards are those with a splitter that is separate from the guard assembly. In most cases, this will mean using a saw with an aftermarket *overarm guard* system installed (See pages 134 to 136).

Making the cut. To rip-cut a thick board in two passes, raise the blade to its full height. Set your overarm guard to ride along the top of the workpiece. Set the rip fence so the blade will cut 1⁄32 in. or so on the waste side of the layout line. Ripping oversize stock will almost certainly leave burn marks on the wood. By sawing outside the layout lines, you can remove burn marks on the jointer or with a hand plane later.

As you make your cuts, feed the wood through the blade as quickly as you can without bogging down the motor to minimize burning. Once you've completed the first cut, flip the workpiece over end-for-end and lower the blade so it cuts just past the top of the first saw kerf. This way, less of the blade will be pinched if the kerf should begin to close up, a common and dangerous occurrence when you saw without a splitter.

Ripping thin boards & laminate

Most standard rip fences hug the saw table tightly enough that you can rip stock as thin as ⅛ in. without difficulty. However, if a gap exists between the saw table and the fence when the fence is locked in position, ripping thinner materials like plastic laminate may pose a problem. Laminate can slip into the joint between the rip fence and the saw table as you cut it.

Before you cut laminate, inspect the fit between the rip fence and saw table, with the fence locked down. If you see a gap, attach an auxiliary wood fence to the rip fence to cover the gap.

Be particularly wary if your saw fence is T-square style (See page 9), in which case the rip fence doesn't clamp to a fence rail along the back of the saw table. If using a T-square fence, attach a C-clamp around the back of the fence and the saw table to hold the fence tight to the table along its full length.

Another concern with rip-cutting laminate or other thin material is that wind generated by the spinning blade may lift the material during cutting. If the laminate starts fluttering against the blade, it will chip. Solve the problem by using a pushstick with a long sole to hold the laminate tight against the saw table near the blade. NOTE: *For best results, use a triple-chip laminate-cutting blade or a sharp crosscut blade to cut laminate cleanly (See pages 48 to 55).*

Auxiliary fence

Gap between rip fence and saw table

Inspect the joint **between the rip fence and saw table with the fence locked down. Before you cut thin stock, like plastic laminate, cover any gaps by bolting an auxiliary fence to your rip fence.**

Hold laminate **or other thin sheet materials firmly against the saw table with a long-soled pushstick to keep the workpiece from lifting or fluttering against the blade as you cut.**

Ripping bevels

Bevel cuts are rip cuts made with the blade tilted to an angle other than 90°. Bevels are cut for a variety of purposes: to "break" a sharp edge along the length of a workpiece; to join two edges or ends together at an angle; or to cut tapered edges, such as when building the center panel on a raised-panel door.

Aside from tilting the blade, the process for making a beveled rip cut is the same as making an ordinary rip cut. However, when you tilt the blade, be sure to set the rip fence on the side of the saw table opposite the direction the blade is tilting. (For instance, on right-tilting saws, set the fence on the left side of the blade.) If the blade tilts toward the fence rather than away from it, you'll trap the wood underneath the blade and against the fence, so it will have nowhere to go if it binds except back at you.

Ripping bevels is easy: tilt the blade to the angle you need, and set the rip fence the correct distance from the blade for your workpiece. It's a bit more difficult to measure off of a tilted blade to set the rip fence than if

Set up beveled rip cuts **so the blade tilts away from the rip fence. This keeps the workpiece from becoming trapped between the fence and the blade. Clamp featherboards to the saw to hold down larger panels.**

the blade is square to the table. To be sure your rip fence is set correctly, start the saw and slide your workpiece up to blade until the teeth just nick the workpiece. Back the board away from the blade and check to see that the nick aligns accurately with the cutting mark you've drawn. Adjust the fence as necessary and proceed with the cut.

Bevel-cutting on-edge

From time to time you'll need to cut bevels at angles exceeding the maximum blade tilt of your saw. In these instances, you'll need to stand the workpiece on edge against the rip fence to cut the bevel. For workpieces taller or wider than about 6 in., attach a tall wooden auxiliary fence to the rip fence to support the workpiece as you cut. Without a tall fence, it's tough to keep a board from teetering away from the fence, which could bind on the blade and lead to kickback.

Any flat, wide scrap of ¾-in.-thick stock will make a suitable tall fence, but it should extend the full length of your rip fence. A tall fence must sit perpendicular to the saw table and should not distort when you attach it to your rip fence. You can build a tall fence that clamps to the saw's rip fence (See pages 148 to 149) or bolt one directly to the rip fence. However it attaches, the tall

Feed the workpiece into the blade until the blade just nicks the board. Use nicks as a guides for adjusting the rip fence until the blade aligns accurately with your bevel layout mark.

fence should be slightly shorter than the workpiece you are cutting, so you can keep a firm grip on the workpiece as you cut. If the beveled edges of the workpiece are narrow, clamp the workpiece to a piece of scrap that rides on top of the rip fence to keep the workpiece from diving into the blade slot opening in the throatplate. Or, install a zero-clearance throatplate (See pages 33 to 34).

Cutting raised panels on the table saw

Featherboard

Beveled edges of a raised-panel door (shown in cutaway)

Raised panels form the center portion of many traditional cabinet and full-sized doors. One face of the panel is beveled on the edges and ends so it can fit in a groove in the surrounding door frame (See the cutaway drawing, above). To cut the panel, you'll need to bevel-rip the workpiece on edge against a tall fence. Clamp on a featherboard to hold the workpiece tight against the fence. Install a zero-clearance throatplate in the saw, or clamp a piece of scrap to the workpiece to ride along the top of the fence.

Ripping tapers

Tapers are modified rip cuts made with a jig that holds the workpieces at an angle to the saw blade. The workpiece starts out square on all faces and edges, but the jig slides along the rip fence and allows the blade to cut into the workpiece at an angle, so one end of the workpiece becomes narrower than the other.

In furniturebuilding, tapering is a fairly common technique for slimming down the profiles of table and chair legs. Tapers are easy cuts to make, but there is no safe way to cut a taper on the table saw without using a jig. Never attempt to cut a taper by setting the rip fence at an angle to the blade or pushing the workpiece freehand through the blade. The wood will kick back.

Tapering jig styles. Tapering jigs can be either fixed or adjustable. Unless you cut many tapers, a simple fixed tapering jig is probably all you need. It's simply a rectangular piece of scrap stock with a cutout area along one edge that matches the taper profile. Follow the directions on the next page to build a fixed tapering jig.

The adjustable variety is just as easy to use as a fixed jig, but it takes a little longer to build. (For instructions on building an adjustable tapering jig, see pages 150 to 151.) You can also buy relatively inexpensive adjustable tapering jigs through most woodworking stores and catalogs.

Adjustable tapering jigs consist of two "arms" about 2 ft. long that are attached together on one end with a hinge. One arm rides against the rip fence, while the other arm supports the workpiece. A stop at the end of the support arm holds the workpiece in position as you slide the jig and workpiece through the blade. An adjustable brace spans the two support arms on top of the jig and holds them at a fixed angle that matches the taper on the workpiece.

ADJUSTABLE TAPERING JIG

Adjustable brace

Scale

To build an adjustable tapering jig, see pages 150 to 151.

Adjustable tapering jigs **can be set to cut tapers of various degrees of shape. Most jigs are made of metal and come with an adjustable brace that spans the "arms" of the jig to lock them in position. Some have a scale for setting taper angles.**

FIXED TAPERING JIG

Workpiece

Jig

Fixed tapering jigs **can be made of any flat, square 3/4-in.-thick panel scrap. A notched cutout area along the edge of the jig establishes the taper angle. To cut a taper, set the workpiece into the notch on the jig and slide the jig along the rip fence. Use a pushstick or scrap to hold the workpiece against the saw table and the jig.**

Building a fixed tapering jig

Fixed tapering jigs begin with a rectangular piece of ¾-in. plywood. The size of the jig depends on the length of the taper you plan to cut. The longer the taper is, the longer the jig will need to be, because the jig marks the full length of the material the saw will remove to form the taper. The jig should be wide enough so there is plenty of material between the tapering area and the flat edge that will ride against the rip fence of your saw.

Using the upper left corner of the plywood as a starting point, measure in along the top edge the thickness of the tapered workpiece at its thickest point. Then measure down the edge of the jig and mark the length of the taper. Measure in straight from that point and mark the thickness of the taper at its narrow end. Connect the points you just made with a straightedge, and cut out the notched area along the outline with a jig saw or band saw. The area you have removed forms the taper profile.

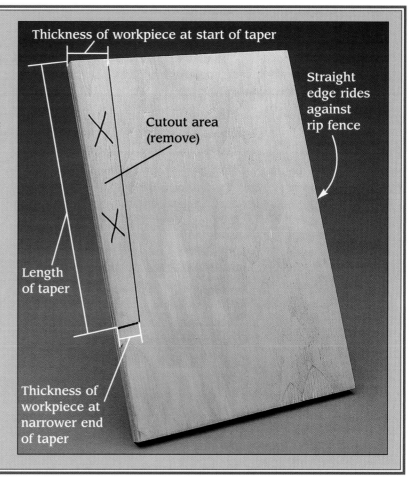

Thickness of workpiece at start of taper

Cutout area (remove)

Straight edge rides against rip fence

Length of taper

Thickness of workpiece at narrower end of taper

Fixed tapering jigs. To use a fixed tapering jig, set the jig on the saw table with the long, flat edge resting against the rip fence. Set the rip fence so the distance between the blade and fence matches the full width of the jig; the blade should only cut into the workpiece—not the jig. Then, raise the blade high enough to cut through the workpiece in one pass. Set the workpiece in the notch and back the jig up on the saw table so the workpiece is clear of the blade. Grab a pushstick to hold the workpiece tight against the jig with your left hand as you push the jig with your right hand. Start the saw and slide the jig forward slowly with your right hand slowly until the blade engages the workpiece. Then, feed the jig steadily along the rip fence, keeping the workpiece held snugly against the jig with a pushstick until the jig clears the blade.

If you want to taper two adjacent faces of the workpiece, flip the tapered edge up, set the workpiece in the jig and make another pass to cut the second taper. In cases where you want to cut a taper on each face of a workpiece, you'll need to temporarily glue the wedges you cut free on the first two tapers back into place to create bearing surfaces for cutting tapers on the third and fourth faces of the workpiece. Hot-melt glue works well for this purpose. Remove the wedges afterward.

Table Saw History

Parks Alert Swing Off Cut Saw (circa 1923)

Swing-blade cutoff saw

Built to be semi-portable, this cutoff saw was unique because the fence was fixed permanently to the saw table. Rather than sliding workpieces over the table, the operator would step down on a foot pedal in front of the saw to swing the arbor and blade across the table and through a board. This belt-driven saw accepted 12-in.-dia. blades and could be purchased in 1923 for $60.

Adjustable tapering jigs. To set up for cutting tapers with an adjustable tapering jig, first mark layout lines on the workpiece to indicate where the taper starts and ends. Raise the blade a couple of inches above the saw table. Lay a long straightedge flat on the saw table and against the side of the blade that faces the rip fence. Draw a line across the saw table to mark the cutting plane of the blade (See photo, right). This will serve as a reference line to align the tapering jig. Then, remove the straightedge and lower the blade below the saw table.

Set the tapering jig against the rip fence and rest the workpiece against the jig. As a unit, slide the rip fence and jig toward the blade, aligning the layout lines on the workpiece with the blade cutting line on the saw table. Lock the rip fence in position. Then, lock the tapering jig to this cutting angle by tightening the jig's crossbrace.

Back the jig and workpiece up so they clear the blade, and raise the blade high enough to cut through the workpiece in one pass. Slide the jig along the rip fence to cut the taper. Use a pushstick or spring clamp to hold the workpiece against the jig as you make the cut. If you need to cut a taper on an adjacent face, the jig is already set to go. Flip the workpiece so the tapered edge faces up and cut a second taper. To taper all four faces, double the cutting angle of the jig when the tapered faces rest against it.

1 Lay a long straightedge flat on the saw table and against the side of the blade that faces the rip fence. Draw a line across the saw table to mark the cutting plane of the blade. This will serve as a reference line to align the tapering jig.

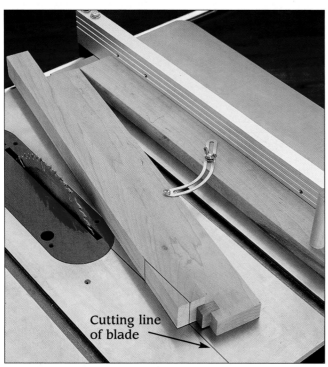

Cutting line of blade

2 Set the tapering jig against the rip fence and rest the workpiece against the jig. Position the rip fence and jig, aligning the layout lines on the workpiece with the line on the saw table. Lock the rip fence in position. Then lock the tapering jig to this cutting angle by tightening the jig's cross brace.

3 Raise the blade to an appropriate height to cut the workpiece all the way through, and cut the taper. Use a pushstick or spring clamp to hold the workpiece against the jig as you make the cut.

Making the cut

Crosscuts

Next to rip cuts, crosscuts are the second most common cuts you'll make on a table saw. Crosscutting is just what its name implies—cutting a workpiece across the grain, which in most cases means cutting a board to length. The basic steps involved in crosscutting on a table saw are setting one long edge of a board against the miter gauge fence, aligning the layout line on the board with the blade, then feeding the board through the blade.

Typically, crosscuts are made after a workpiece has been ripped to width. One crosscut is made to square the end of the board, then a second crosscut saws the board to length. You'll rarely perform rip cuts on a workpiece without then following up with a couple of crosscuts.

Safer cuts. Crosscuts are considerably safer to make than rip cuts for one main reason: You'll use the miter gauge, not the rip fence, as your guide. Remember that ripping involves sandwiching a workpiece in between the rip fence and the blade, where it can bind, get caught on the saw teeth at the back of the blade and kick back. Crosscutting, on the other hand, doesn't restrict the clear space around the workpiece. In fact, the rip fence shouldn't even touch the workpiece during a crosscut while the blade is engaged in the wood.

One kind of kickback can occur when crosscutting, but it is the waste piece—not the workpiece—that poses the hazard. Unlike the strips of waste produced by rip cuts, which typically are long enough to be kept clear of the blade by the splitter, crosscutting often creates short pieces of waste that sit right next to the blade when they are cut free. If you don't use a zero-clearance throatplate on the saw, small waste pieces can get pulled down into the gap between the blade and the throatplate. If this happens near the back of the blade, the teeth on the outfeed side of the blade could lift the waste and throw it back in your direction. A blade guard and a zero-clearance throatplate will significantly reduce the chances of injury from this kind of kickback.

> **CAUTION:**
> *Some of the photographs you'll see throughout this book show the blade guard and splitter removed. This was done to make the information in the photographs easier to see. To prevent injury, use a working blade guard and a splitter with antikickback pawls whenever the type of cut being made allows it.*

Crosscutting, or sawing wood across the grain, serves two purposes: it squares the ends of workpieces and trims them to length. You'll perform these cuts with workpieces held against the miter gauge.

Table Saw History

Revolving twin-arbor saw

Built to meet the sawing needs of cabinet, pattern, sash and carriage shops in the early 1900s, this saw featured a double arbor cradle that pivoted on a center shaft so the saw could be outfitted with two blades—one for crosscutting and the other for ripping. A crank below the saw table revolved either type of 14-in.-dia. blade into position. The saw table tilted left and right up to 45° for making bevel cuts. The right side of the cast-iron table was fixed in position for making rip cuts, but the left side, outfitted with twin mitering fences, actually slid past the blade on rollers for making crosscuts.

J. A. Fay & Co. Double Circular Sawing Machine (circa 1903)

Crosscutting with a miter gauge

Most crosscuts are intended to square the ends of workpieces. To make these cuts accurately, first set the miter fence perpendicular to the miter bar with a square. While you're at it, use a square to make sure that the saw blade is perpendicular to the saw table. Once the blade is square to the table, lower it to a height suitable for cutting through the workpiece. Be sure the splitter is aligned with the blade.

Setting up the cut

It doesn't matter which miter slot you choose for making square crosscuts with the miter gauge. If one of the two miter slots on your saw is milled closer to the blade than the other, choose the closer slot for crosscutting, so the miter fence will support the workpiece as close to the blade as possible. The closer you can support the workpiece to the blade, the less likely it will be to shift away from the blade as you cut.

Draw layout lines across both the face and leading edge of the board (the edge that will make contact with the blade first). With the saw turned off, set one flat edge of the workpiece against the miter fence and slide the miter gauge forward on the saw table until the cutting line on the edge of the board touches the blade. Align the layout lines with the blade so that the blade will cut on the waste side of the workpiece.

Once you've aligned the board with the blade, clamp or hold the workpiece in position against the miter fence. Stand behind the miter gauge so you are clear of the path of the blade. If you hold, rather than clamp, the workpiece to the miter gauge, wrap your hand around the fence to grip the work and push the gauge forward with your other hand on the miter fence lock knob. This way, your arms should not cross the blade at any time during a cut.

Making the cut

Start the saw, slide the miter gauge forward slowly until the blade enters the wood, then increase your feed rate to cut quickly and cleanly through the workpiece without stopping. Continue pushing the miter gauge forward until it completely passes the blade.

As soon as the full workpiece passes the infeed side of the blade, the waste piece will be cut free and stop next to the spinning blade. Do not let waste pieces accumulate here. If the waste is just a sliver, the blade will probably blow it out of the way or suck it down the blade slot opening in the throatplate. Larger cutoffs will sit on the table or may even rattle against the blade. It's important to clear these waste pieces away from the blade to keep them from accidentally catching on the blade, but only if they are large enough to be removed safely while the blade is spinning. Use a pushstick to slide cutoffs shorter than 6 in. away from the blade. If

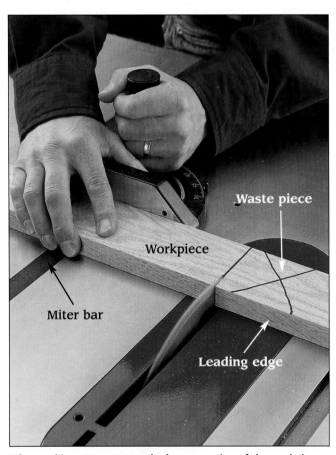

When making crosscuts, set the longer section of the workpiece against the miter gauge and cut the shorter portion free. Usually, the part you hold against the miter gauge will be your workpiece rather than a waste piece. Align the blade so it cuts on the waste side, rather than the workpiece side, of the board.

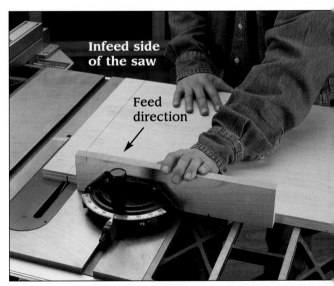

If you are crosscutting a panel that is too wide to be fed into the blade with the miter gauge in back of the board, position the gauge ahead of the panel instead. Attach an auxiliary fence to the miter gauge to provide more support. Feed the panel across the blade as usual, from the infeed side of the saw.

you can't remove waste pieces easily with a pushstick, shut off the saw and brush them away once the blade has stopped.

Improving miter gauge performance

Although a miter gauge makes crosscutting safer, it doesn't necessarily make crosscuts precisely. Most miter gauges come with fences that are only about 6 in. long, sometimes even less. The trouble is, most workpieces you'll need to crosscut will be longer than the miter gauge fence. The longer the workpiece, the harder time you'll have holding it tight against the short miter fence as you feed it through the blade. This is because the center of gravity of a board is near the middle, which moves further and further away from the miter gauge the closer to the end of the board you cut (See *Illustration*, below). The weight of the board acts like a lever against the short portion you are clamping or holding against the miter fence. Result? Long workpieces tend to pivot away from the miter gauge fence toward their center of gravity. The instant this happens, your cut will shift away from the layout line, ruining your accuracy.

The problem here boils down to poor workpiece support, but you can solve miter gauge limitations in three fairly easy ways: (1) Add an auxiliary fence to the miter gauge, (2) Build a shooting board, or (3) Build a crosscut sled.

Adding an auxiliary miter fence

Most miter gauge fence bodies come with two holes drilled through the fence for adding an auxiliary wooden fence. The auxiliary fence will get chewed up by the blade, so it's an easy item to periodically replace. To make one, select a piece of dimensionally stable scrapwood (hardwood, medium-density fiberboard or plywood) about 2 ft. long,

Squaring board ends

When squaring up the end of a board, **make the cut far enough in from the end so there is a significant amount of wood on either side of the blade. Don't shave board ends. A table saw is a cutting tool—not a shaving tool. If cutting stresses aren't distributed evenly on both sides of the blade, especially on thin-kerf blades, the blade will deflect. Once the blade deflects, your cut won't be square. Check the cut end with a square to verify that it is actually square to the board's edges and faces.**

The closer you cut to the end of a workpiece, **the further away its center of gravity moves from the miter gauge. Without an auxiliary fence attached to the miter gauge, the workpiece will pivot at its center of gravity like a lever, away from the miter fence.**

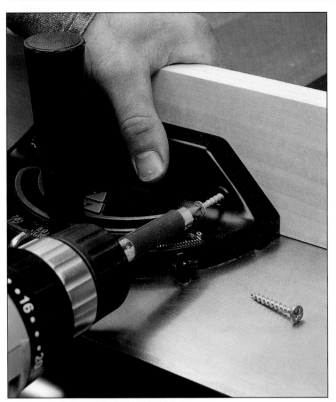

Adding an auxiliary fence. Most miter gauge fences are outfitted with a pair of holes to accommodate screws for attaching an auxiliary fence. Select a flat piece of scrapwood or plywood for the auxiliary fence. Set the miter gauge in a miter gauge slot on the saw table. Attach the fence with short wood screws so it sits flush with the saw table. Screws should be short enough so they don't pierce the front of the fence.

¾ to 1 in. thick and about 1 in. wider than the saw's full blade height above the table. The auxiliary fence should be flat on both faces and square on at least one long edge.

You have two choices for building auxiliary miter fences—*flush-style* or *sweep-style.* Flush-style auxiliary fences stop just short of the saw guard, so the guard doesn't have to ride up and over the fence when you make a cut.

Sweep-style miter fences extend about 6 in. or so past the blade, so they provide better workpiece support around the blade than flush-style fences. Plus, the added fence length beyond the blade will sweep waste pieces clear when you push the miter gauge through the cut.

Since the saw kerf on a sweep-style fence matches the blade kerf exactly, use the kerf on the fence to align the cut lines on your workpieces with the blade. Be aware, however, that the guard on your saw will have to travel up and over a sweep-style fence, because it straddles the blade. If the guard on your saw cannot rise up and over the sweep fence, attach a flush-style fence instead. Do not solve this problem by removing your saw's guard and splitter.

To attach either fence style, choose screws short enough so the tips do not pierce the front face of the auxiliary fence. Tɪᴘ: *Cut a piece of medium-grit sandpaper sized to cover the fence face and use spray-mount adhesive or glue to adhere it to the fence, grit side facing out. Sandpaper will give the fence "tooth" for a better grip on workpieces.*

Common auxiliary miter fence styles

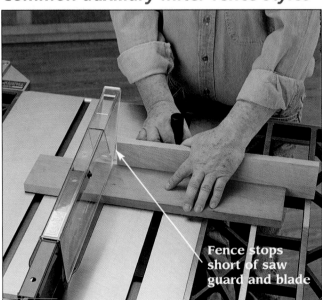

Fence stops short of saw guard and blade

Flush-style miter fences stop short of the blade guard to keep the guard from riding up and over the fence. This style also keeps the fence clear of the posts that mount the guard to the splitter, which would obstruct the path of the miter gauge.

Overarm-style blade guard

Fence extends underneath saw guard and past blade

Sweep-style miter fences extend past the blade and provide a sweeping effect for waste pieces, once they are cut free. Your saw guard will have to ride up and over the fence, so this fence style is best suited for overarm-style blade guards.

Shooting boards

Workpieces longer than 2 ft. are tricky to cross-cut accurately on a table saw. When workpieces extend past the ends of your auxiliary miter fence, they become progressively harder to manage. Depending upon how long your workpiece is and where along its length you plan to make your cut, it will be tough to hold the workpiece steady against even a long auxiliary miter fence. One solution to this problem is to add a support device alongside the saw, but you'll still have to drag the workpiece across the saw table to cut it when guiding it with the miter gauge. Another option is to build a jig that supports the workpiece from beneath, called a *shooting board.* (Shooting boards are also commonly known as *panel-cutting jigs.*)

A shooting board can replace the miter gauge for crosscuts on longer or wider workpieces. It consists of a piece of plywood with a hardwood runner that slides in one of the two miter slots on the saw table (See *Illustration,* below). The jig's plywood base can be as large as half the saw table, including an extension wing. The bigger, the better. Shooting boards are equipped with a long fence along the trailing edge of the jig base to provide a surface that holds

Shooting boards provide a more stable support system for cutting long workpieces because the workpiece actually rides on top of the jig rather than sliding on the saw table. A long fence on the back of the jig keeps larger workpieces square with the blade. The jig rides on a hardwood runner that fits in the miter slot.

Building a shooting board

Cut the base of the shooting board from a piece of ¾-in. cabinet-grade plywood, melamine-covered particleboard or medium-density fiberboard. Size the base so it covers the full depth of your saw table and is a couple inches longer than the distance from the blade to the outer edge of one extension wing. Cut the miter slot runner from hardwood. The runner should slide in the miter slot without binding and be flush with the surface of the saw table. Slip the runner into the miter slot. The shooting board base piece should be positioned so one end of the base extends past the blade about an inch. Square the base to the front edge of the saw table. Mark the position of the runner on the base, and attach the runner to the base with short countersunk wood screws. Set the base and runner in the miter slot again and trim the end of the jig base so it is flush with the blade. Cut the fence from a piece of 2- to 3-in.-wide hardwood. The fence length should match the length of the base. Use a carpenter's square against the "blade" end of the base to square the fence along the front edge of the base. Attach the fence to the base with 1¼-in. countersunk wood screws.

Aligning a workpiece on a shooting board. It's easy to precisely align a workpiece cutting line with the blade on a shooting board, because the edge of the jig is flush with the side of the blade. Align the workpiece cutting line with the edge of the shooting board base, hold the workpiece against the fence and make your cut. You'll need to raise the blade high enough to account for the thickness of the jig base in order to cut through the workpiece in one pass.

Table Saw History

Bentel & Margedant Co. Railway Cut Off Saw (circa 1890)

Crosscut saw manufactured to build railways

Built in the 1890s to meet the sawing needs of America's growing railroad system, this massive 1250-pound machine likely cross-cut timbers used for railroad ties. The saw featured a sliding tabletop for feeding timbers into the blade. The main drive belt could be adjusted on a cone-shaped pulley to change blade speed.

the workpiece. The fence also allows you to spread your arms apart when you push the jig, distributing the pushing action more evenly between both arms.

A shooting board outperforms a miter gauge for making crosscuts because it carries a workpiece across the saw table rather than sliding it on the table as a miter gauge does. Dragging the workpiece over the saw table is the main reason why workpieces shift during typical miter gauge cuts.

When you construct a shooting board, you'll trim the jig so one end of the base and the fence are flush with the blade (See page 83). With this arrangement, aligning crosscuts is easy. Simply set the workpiece on the shooting board so the cutting line and the edge of the fence match up. This way the blade will cut up to and on the waste side of your cutting line.

Making crosscuts with a shooting board

Before you start the saw, be sure the blade guard will rise up and over the vertical fence on the shooting board. Back the shooting board up on the saw table so the shooting board is clear of the blade. Stand out of line with the blade behind the shooting board. Start the saw and slide the board forward until the blade engages the workpiece, then slide the shooting board and workpiece smoothly past the blade.

The waste piece will drop next to the blade as soon you finish the cut. Unless the waste piece is at least 6 in. long, avoid the temptation to slide it away from the blade with your hand or flick it away with a pushstick. The safest method for clearing away a short cutoff scrap is to shut down the saw, wait until the blade stops and slide the waste away from the blade with a pushstick before you pick it up.

Crosscut sleds

Crosscutting with a crosscut sled is like using a pair of shooting boards in tandem on either side of the blade. Unlike a shooting board, which only supports a workpiece on one side of the blade, a crosscut sled cradles both the workpiece and the waste piece.

The sled has a multitude of uses, and you'll see different examples of its versatility throughout this book, but it shines as the superior crosscutting jig. You can use it in place of the miter gauge for typical crosscuts or even for making miter-cuts if you add a simple mitering attachment (See page 90). A crosscut sled is especially handy when you need to crosscut long workpieces that will produce long, unwieldy cutoffs. When you use a shooting board for the same task, long cutoffs will drop next to the blade as soon as they are cut free, where they could accidentally come into contact with the blade or even tip off the saw table. This won't happen on a crosscut sled. Even when the waste piece is cut free, it still rests on the sled base.

Crosscut sleds **provide support for workpieces on both sides of the blade, which is especially helpful for crosscutting long pieces of lumber into two long sections. After you make the cut, both lengths of stock are still supported from beneath. Clamp a scrap block against the sled fence to keep workpieces held snugly against the sled base.**

Crosscut sled features

Most crosscut sleds have basically the same design. A crosscut sled starts out as a piece of plywood about the size of the full saw table plus extension wings. It has two shooting board-style runners fastened below to ride in the miter slots. A tall fence spans either long edge of the sled. Once the jig is made, you'll raise the saw blade and cut a kerf across the entire width of the sled and through the fences to create a blade track. See pages 145 to 147 for a complete set of plans to build the crosscut sled you'll see featured in this book.

The fence on the infeed side of the sled serves the same purpose as the fence on the shooting board—to support, align and anchor workpieces. The fence on the outfeed side of the jig bridges the gap created by the saw kerf and holds the two plywood base pieces in place. Since the sled covers the full saw table, the jig fences will interfere with most saw guard and splitter assemblies. Unless your guard mounts from the extreme left- or right-hand side of the saw, you'll have to remove these safety items in order to use a crosscut sled.

Some crosscut sled designs incorporate safety features to shield you from blade exposure. The crosscut sled plans featured in this book include information for constructing a simple blade guard and blade tunnel. If the plans you build from do not call for a blade guard, add one. Without a blade guard, a crosscut sled does nothing to protect you from blade injuries.

Using a sled

To use the sled, set your workpiece against the infeed fence, aligning the cutting line on the workpiece with the saw kerf in the fence. Clamp or hold the workpiece tightly to the fence. If your workpiece is narrow, you may be able to start the saw with the blade inside the sled. This is perfectly safe, provided the blade guard is in position and there is plenty of space between the front edge of the workpiece and the blade. For wide panels, you'll have to start the cut with the crosscut sled pulled in front of the blade.

Stand to the right or left of the blade, behind the side of the sled that supports the heaviest part of what you are cutting. Slide the sled across the table until the blade cuts through the board. Turn off the saw and remove both cut pieces. If you are making repetitive cuts and do not want to shut the saw down between cuts, slide the workpiece and waste piece away from the saw kerf in the sled and remove the waste piece. Then, pull the sled back toward yourself to set up for the next cut. Do not let waste pieces accumulate in the sled, where they could accidentally come in contact with the blade.

Side support options

Sawhorse extension. Adding side support doesn't have to be fancy—just stable. One easy option is to screw a couple of short legs to a length of scrap stock, then clamp the assembly to the top of a sawhorse at whatever saw table height you need.

Outfeed table. Build the outfeed table shown on pages 154 to 155 and use it as a side support device as well as an outfeed table. This accessory clamps into the vise of a portable workbench, so its height is fully adjustable. If you don't own a portable workbench, you could also clamp the jig to a sawhorse.

The techniques you use for making safe, accurate crosscuts will need to change somewhat to accommodate workpieces of different proportions. You'll also want to modify your crosscutting approach when you pivot the miter gauge to make mitered cuts. The next few pages cover a number of specialized crosscutting situations and procedures you should follow for making these cuts:

Crosscutting long boards

Crosscutting a 6- or 8-ft. board is cumbersome and tough to do with great precision using just the miter gauge as a guide. Longer boards will become even more unwieldy on the table saw. Power miter saws are gaining popularity by both contractors and woodworkers because these tools allow you to hold a long board stationary and pull the saw blade through them, rather than the other way around as you must do on the table saw. For extremely long stock, choose the most suitable saw for the job. In some cases, a power miter saw, circular saw or even a crosscut hand saw may make more sense than horsing a long board over a short saw table. You can always cut long stock into shorter segments with one of these saws, then make final crosscuts on the table saw.

Reinforcing a miter fence

Stiffen long auxiliary miter fences to keep them from deflecting by attaching a wood spine perpendicular to the back of the fence. The spine should be narrow enough so it doesn't obstruct the miter gauge handle.

When your only option is to cross-cut a long board on the table saw, use a shooting board or crosscut sled to support as much of the board on the saw table as you can. Or, fasten a long auxiliary fence to the miter gauge. Strengthen the auxiliary miter fence with a wood spine to keep it from deflecting (See *Tip*, previous page). If a workpiece extends more than a couple feet over the edge of the saw table, set up a tall sawhorse or another worktable next to the saw to support the workpiece as you make your cut.

Crosscutting short stock

Whenever you can, cross-cut a workpiece from a piece of stock long enough to handle safely. It's not always practical to do this, however, if all you have to work with is a short piece of stock. In situations where your hand would need to come within 6 in. of the blade to hold a workpiece for a crosscut, make the cut on a shooting board or crosscut sled instead of using only the miter gauge. A short workpiece is more likely to shift when dragged over the saw table against a miter fence, especially if you have to hold it down with a pushstick as you feed the workpiece into the blade. Hold the short piece in place on the shooting board or crosscut sled with a rubber-soled pushpad, a piece of scrap or a pushstick.

Crosscutting short stock. The safest method for crosscutting short stock is to make the cut on a crosscut sled. Keep your hand a safe distance from the blade by holding the workpiece with a rubber-soled pushpad, a piece of scrap wood or a pushstick. If you don't have a crosscut sled, cross-cut short workpieces from longer lengths of stock—never risk your fingers by holding workpieces shorter than 6 in. by hand.

Making repetitive crosscuts

Frequently you'll need to cross-cut a number of workpieces to the same length for a project. You could measure these parts out one by one and cross-cut each part to length, but this method is time-consuming. Plus, parts cut to length this way seldom match.

A faster and more accurate method for making repetitive crosscuts on a table saw is to use a stopblock. A stopblock is simply a piece of scrap with square faces and edges that's large enough to be clamped in place on the saw. The common places to clamp a stopblock are to the rip fence, an auxiliary fence on a miter gauge or to the fence on a shooting board or crosscut sled. You'll clamp the stopblock a precise distance away from the blade, then position one end of the workpiece against the stopblock, using the stopblock as an index for aligning the blade with your cutting line. This way, you only have to measure once to establish a fixed length for cutting as many pieces as you need.

When using a stopblock attached to an auxiliary miter gauge fence or the fence on the crosscut sled or shooting board, clamp the stopblock to the fence on the same side of the blade as the workpiece. The distance from the stopblock to the blade should match the

Stopblock

Making repetitive crosscuts with a miter fence. Clamp a stopblock to an auxiliary miter fence and use the block as a guide for cross-cutting many workpieces to the same length. The distance from the near side of the blade to the stopblock equals the length of your workpiece, once it's cross-cut to size.

Making repetitive crosscuts with the rip fence. **Clamp a stop block to the rip fence on the infeed side of the blade. Clamp the block far enough back from the blade so your workpiece will clear the stop block before the blade engages it. This set-up will provide a clear space between the rip fence and the end of the workpiece. The distance from the stop block to the blade equals the length of the workpieces, once they are cut to size.**

Making beveled crosscuts. **Set up beveled crosscuts so the blade tilts away from the miter gauge. This way, waste pieces will rest against the saw table once they are cut free rather than on top of the blade, where they could catch on the blade teeth and shoot back.**

finished length of the workpiece. If the workpiece length exceeds the length of the auxiliary fence, install a longer fence.

As a guide for making repetitive crosscuts, you can also clamp a stopblock to the rip fence. The stopblock should be on the infeed side of the blade, near the front of the saw table. Be sure the stopblock is at least ¾ in. thick. This cutting situation is the only time it is safe to use the miter gauge and the rip fence in tandem when cutting a board into parts. The distance from the stopblock to the blade sets the length of the workpieces. The stopblock also provides a space between the end of the workpiece and the rip fence. Without this space, the cutoff piece would be trapped between the rip fence, miter fence and the blade, which could result in kickback.

To set up a stopblock on the rip fence, clamp the stopblock far enough forward on the infeed side of the rip fence so the workpiece will clear the stopblock before it makes contact with the blade. Set the workpiece against the miter gauge and slide it along the miter fence until the cutting line aligns with the blade. Hold the workpiece in this position and pull the miter gauge back to the front of the saw table. Slide the rip fence over until the stopblock touches the end of the workpiece, then lock the rip fence in position. Before you make each cut, be sure the workpiece touches the stopblock.

Crosscutting bevels

The setup for beveled crosscuts is nearly the same as for square crosscuts, except the blade is set an angle other than 90°. When setting up a beveled crosscut, it's important to use the miter slot that faces away from the direction of blade tilt. For instance, if the blade tilts to the right, make the cut with the miter gauge on the left side of the blade. The object here is to cut the workpiece so the waste is below the blade, not above it. If the waste piece ends up on top of the blade once it's cut free, it could catch on the blade and kick back.

Cutting miters

Cutting miters involves swiveling the protractor-style miter gauge head so it is no longer perpendicular to the blade. The most common miter setting is 45°, but miter gauges can be adjusted to any angle up to 45°. Unless you are using a precision miter gauge (See page 137), don't trust that the scale on your miter gauge is accurate. For maximum accuracy, use a drafting triangle or bevel gauge set against the blade and miter gauge to establish exact angles. If you want to match an angle already scribed on your workpiece, lay the miter gauge head against a flat edge of the workpiece and swivel the miter bar until it matches the angle on the workpiece. Once you've determined the miter angle and set the protractor head, it never hurts to make a test cut on a scrap piece before cutting your workpiece.

The only potentially frustrating part of making miter cuts is that it's tougher to hold a workpiece steady against the miter gauge with the head at an angle than when the head is square to the blade. Boards will want to creep away from the blade along the miter fence in response to forces imposed by the blade and friction from the saw table. The steeper the miter angle setting, the worse your control will become. It's tough to make accurate miters without first attaching an auxiliary fence to the miter gauge.

Making miter-cuts. Attach an auxiliary fence to the miter gauge to support your workpiece right up to the blade. For best control when miter-cutting, set up your cuts so the cut end leads the rest of the workpiece across the table, as shown above.

Methods for setting a miter gauge

Use the workpiece cutting line. When the angle you need to cut is already marked on your workpiece, match the angle on the miter gauge by setting the bar along your layout line and the protractor head flush against one edge of the workpiece. With this method, you'll have to flip the workpiece layout-side down on the saw table to orient it properly on the miter gauge, so mark both workpiece faces.

Use a bevel gauge to set angles. In cases where you want to cut a miter to match an odd angle taken from another source, use a bevel gauge to mark the angle you need. Then, set the bevel gauge base against the saw blade and swivel the miter gauge fence until it is flush with the bevel gauge arm. Lock the miter gauge at this angle.

When you can, it's best to orient the workpiece on the miter gauge so the cut will lead the workpiece past the blade, rather than follow behind it. Pushing the cut ahead of the rest of the workpiece will keep you from reaching further than you need to over the saw. You'll also have better hand control over the workpiece.

TIP: *Improve the accuracy of your miter cuts by attaching sandpaper to the miter gauge fence.* Or, you can build a simple mitering attachment for your crosscut sled to hold workpieces at a 45° angle to the sled fence (See *Tip,* below).

Attach a stopblock to the miter fence if you need to make repetitive miter cuts, just as you would when making repetitive square crosscuts. If a stopblock needs to support an end that's already mitered, it must stand out far enough from the fence to make contact with the tip of the miter. When you can, set the mitered end of a workpiece so it tapers toward the fence, rather than away from it. Clamp an angled stopblock against the workpiece to capture the mitered end of the workpiece against the fence (See photo, right).

Making repetitive miter cuts with a stopblock. You can make repetitive miter cuts by clamping a stopblock to the miter gauge fence, just as you would if you were making repetitive crosscuts. If one end of each workpiece is already cut at an angle, capture the mitered end against the auxiliary miter fence with a stopblock cut at a complementary angle.

Mitering jig for crosscut sleds

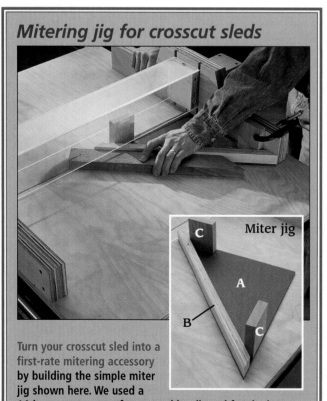

Miter jig

Turn your crosscut sled into a first-rate mitering accessory by building the simple miter jig shown here. We used a 14-in.-square scrap of tempered hardboard for the base (A), cut diagonally into the shape of a 45° triangle. Attach a fence (B) along the long edge of the hardboard and a couple of scrap blocks (C) behind the fence on each end. The blocks serve as clamping points for holding the miter jig in place on the sled. To use the mitering attachment, clamp the square corner of the jig base against the sled fence so one short edge of the jig is flush with the saw kerf in the sled.

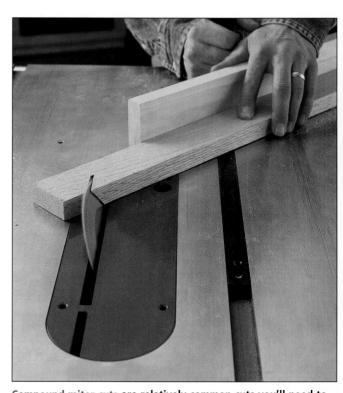

Compound miter cuts are relatively common cuts you'll need to make for projects such as installing cove and crown molding. To make a compound miter cut, you'll tilt the blade and swivel the miter gauge head to cut two angles at once. Test your set up on a scrap piece before committing to your actual workpiece.

Cutting sheet goods safely

From time to time, your wood-working or home improvement projects will require you to use manufactured sheet goods, such as medium-density fiberboard (MDF), hardboard, particleboard or various kinds of plywoods. These products have several advantages over board lumber: they don't expand or contract to the same degree as wood; and they have no grain direction, so they aren't prone to twisting and warping like actual lumber. Plus, sheet goods typically come in 4 × 8-ft. panels, which enable you to create large panels without having to glue a number of boards together.

In spite of its advantages as a building material, full-sized sheets of plywood or particleboard are heavy to lift and can be unwieldy to control, especially if you are working alone. Weight and workpiece proportions are the main issues you'll have to contend with when sawing sheet goods on a table saw.

Sheet goods **come in a wide variety of compositions to suit a host of different wood-working and construction applications. With proper cutting techniques and sturdy workpiece support, you can cut them safely on the table saw.**

Pointers for safer, smoother cuts

Sheet stock can be broken down safely and accurately on the table saw, but here are a few rules of thumb to keep in mind:

1. Start with manageable workpieces

Many woodworkers cut 4 × 8 sheets into smaller pieces with a circular saw or jig saw first to make them more manageable on the table saw. This is an especially good practice to follow if you are using a bench-top saw with a small table, or if you don't have a number of sturdy worktables, roller stands or saw-horses handy to support your work. Lay out a piece of sheet stock so you'll make the longest rip cuts and crosscuts first. This way, you'll first break the sheets down into reasonable pieces. Then subdivide the smaller pieces into individual parts on the table saw.

2. Guards and splitters are a must

Larger sheet panels will require you to start your cuts farther away from the saw, which makes it harder to keep a large workpiece tight to the rip fence. The problem compounds if you are also straining to support a heavy panel or if the panel is thin and starts to bow. If the workpiece drifts away from the rip fence, you are at

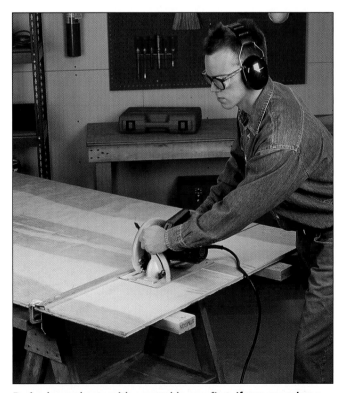

Resize large sheets with a portable saw first. **If you are using a small benchtop table saw or you don't have a way to support your workpiece adequately around the table saw, start by cutting full-sized sheets down to more manageable proportions with a circular saw and straightedge guide.**

Supporting sheet goods

Ripping. When ripping larger sheets, be sure to support the work-piece as the cut is completed. Roller stands will work, but a broad surface, like a shop table, provides even better support.

Crosscutting. Roller stands aren't suitable for supporting long panels when crosscutting. You'll need a support device long enough to span the depth of the saw table and beyond.

Using a helper for outfeed support

Saw operator

Helper

Enlist a helper to act as outfeed support if no other tempo-rary support is available. As a workpiece leaves the saw table, a helper should cup the front edge of the board with both hands (but not grip it) and walk backward, keeping pace with the rate you are feeding wood into the saw. It is unsafe for a helper to pull or steer the workpiece; you as the operator must remain in complete control of the cut.

a greater risk for kickback, so always saw sheet goods with a guard and splitter in place on the saw. A splitter will help to keep a panel from binding against the saw blade during long rip cuts.

3. Provide sturdy workpiece support

For large panels of sheet stock, workpiece support is crucial. The best setup for cutting full-sized sheets is to outfit a table saw with a large outfeed table butted against or attached to the back of the saw. A 4- to 6-ft. or longer outfeed table will provide plenty of support for an 8-ft. length of sheet stock, once it exits the blade. (Be sure the outfeed table is wide enough to accommo-date both the workpiece and the waste piece.) You can also use several roller or ball-bearing-style stands set behind the saw instead of an outfeed table, but be sure they have stable footings and are lined up squarely with the saw. Roller stands that have cylinders for rollers can skew, tip or skid along the floor if a heavy piece of sheet stock rolls over them at an angle. A bet-ter roller stand for sheet stock uses cupped ball bear-ings rather than long cylinders for rollers. Ball-bearings roll in any direction, so it doesn't matter whether the workpiece contacts them straight on or at an angle.

4. Keep longer edges against a fence

Never rip-cut a panel with the shorter edge against the rip fence, especially if the width is less than 12 in. The rip fence will not provide enough support for the panel you are cutting, and the workpiece could creep away from the fence, bind against the blade and kick back. Use a miter gauge outfitted with a long auxiliary

Stable crosscutting. Cross-cut sleds are a better alternative than a miter gauge and auxiliary miter fence for crosscutting wider panels. Since the sled completely supports the panel from beneath, it cannot pivot or shift as you make the cut. If you are crosscutting panels considerably longer than the saw table, you'll need to provide additional workpiece support along-side the saw, even when using a crosscut sled.

fence to crosscut long, narrow panels. Better still, lay them on a shooting board or crosscut sled to make the cut (See photo, above).

5. Reinforce or lengthen your rip fence

Larger panels of sheet stock will place more stress on the rip fence as you are making rip cuts. If the rip fence on your saw is T-square style (there is no fence rail along the back of the saw table) or prone to fall out of alignment with the blade, clamp the outfeed end of the fence against the saw table to hold it securely in place.

You can improve the amount of support the rip fence provides by attaching a long auxiliary rip fence (See photo, right). Choose a thick piece of hardwood for the fence to keep it from deflecting. Extending the rip fence is especially helpful if you need to rip large panels of sheet goods on a small benchtop saw. In any case, have the auxiliary fence extend beyond the saw table and onto your outfeed support.

Long auxiliary rip fence

Rip-cutting long panels. Attaching a long auxiliary rip fence will provide more bearing surface when ripping long panels. A long auxiliary rip fence is especially helpful for negotiating sheet goods over a benchtop table saw. For best results, extend the rip fence beyond the back edge of the saw table and onto your outfeed support table.

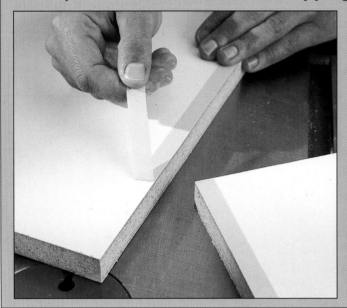

Sheet goods covered with thin veneers, melamine or laminate are prone to tearout and chipping around the blade slot opening in the throatplate. To keep this from happening, install a zero-clearance throatplate in the saw (See pages 33 to 34) and use a sharp triple-chip, crosscut or plywood blade. Since table saws tend to tear wood fibers on the bottom face of a workpiece where the blade exits the wood, place the "good" face of the panel up on the saw table. If both sides of the panel need smooth, chip-free edges, run a strip of masking tape along the cutting line on the bottom of the panel before you make the cut. The tape will keep the veneer, melamine or laminate from splintering or chipping.

Table Saw History

Parks Planing Mill Special (circa 1923)

All-in-one shop tool

Available to carpenters and woodworking shops in the 1920s, this belt-driven, multipurpose machine was outfitted with three table saws—a combination crosscut and rip saw (right-hand side of engraving) and a swing cutoff saw (left back corner). A truly all-in-one workstation touted by the manufacturer as "eight machines in one," the planing mill was also equipped with a band saw, 12-in. jointer, tenoner, upright hollow chisel mortiser and borer, reversible spindle shaper and sanding disk.

Ripping full-sized sheets

The procedure for ripping sheet stock is similar to ripping board lumber, but you'll begin the cut further back and to the left of the saw for cutting full-sized sheets. The object is to feed sheet stock into the blade with your right hand, while keeping the workpiece held against the fence with your left hand.

Starting the cut

Set the rip fence as you would for any rip cut. It's a good practice to attach a long auxiliary fence to the rip fence, to increase the rip fence's bearing surface. Extend the fence onto your outfeed table.

Begin the cut by tipping the sheet up and onto the infeed side of the table. Position yourself behind the sheet near the left corner with your left hand wrapped around the long outside edge, about 1 ft. from the end, and your right hand gripping the end of the sheet at arm's reach. Begin to feed the sheet into the saw, pushing forward with your right hand in a straight line with the blade. Apply diagonal force to the sheet on the infeed side of the rip fence with your left hand, keeping your eye on the joint between the rip fence and the workpiece. It doesn't take much to skew the sheet away from the rip fence, so make any changes in hand or body position gradually. Keep the sheet sliding flat on the saw table at all times.

Shift body position as you near the saw

Increase your feed rate once the cut has begun, keeping your motions fluid. As the end of the sheet nears the the front of the saw, shift position from the left corner of the sheet around to the back edge, moving your right arm so it guides the section of the workpiece between the blade and the rip fence. Slide your left hand closer to the left corner of the sheet so you can maintain some diagonal pressure between the sheet and the rip fence. In those cases where the distance between the rip fence and the blade is wider than about 1 ft., it's safe to use your right hand to feed the workpiece past the blade. Use a pushstick in your right hand for narrower workpieces.

Complete the cut

Once the blade separates the waste piece from the workpiece, continue to guide the workpiece through and past the blade with your right hand or with a pushstick. Use your left hand to hold the waste piece against the table so it doesn't accidentally rub against the blade. Both the waste piece and the workpiece should be supported as they are fed off the saw table with roller stands, an outfeed table or a helper.

1 To begin the cut, stand next to the sheet at the left rear corner. Tip the sheet up onto the saw and feed with your right hand. Apply diagonal force with your left hand to keep the sheet sliding snugly against the rip fence.

2 As the end of the sheet reaches the saw table, shift your body from the left corner around to the back of the panel. Place your right hand on the panel near the edge that rides the rip fence. Continue feeding the sheet through the blade.

3 When the blade cuts the sheet in two, hold the cutoff piece stationary with your left hand. Slide the section of panel between the blade and rip fence completely past the blade with your right hand.

Cutting cove molding

You can cut cove molding or curved beveled edges for raised panels on the table saw using a simple adjustable parallelogram jig and a fine-toothed plywood blade. The technique for cutting coves on the table saw involves passing the workpiece over the blade at an angle so the curvature of the blade matches the cove profile you want. In a sense, the table saw blade will act more like a shaping tool than a cutting tool. By varying the angle of approach on the blade, you can machine any number of cove curvatures, from steep recesses with tight radii to gentle, shallow arcs.

Since the saw blade will act as a makeshift shaper and sander when cutting coves, it is important to use a blade with small, rigid teeth. To keep the blade from deflecting due to the lateral forces you'll be applying to the blade, cutting coves will require that you slow down your feed rate when passing workpieces over the blade. In addition, cutting each cove shape involves making multiple passes over the blade, increasing the blade height by not more than 1/16 in. with each pass, from start to finish.

Build a parallelogram jig

You'll need to build an adjustable parallelogram jig from scrapwood to set up cove cuts. Make the long sides of the jig about 4 ft. long, and the short ends about 1 ft. long. Attach the parts with short carriage bolts, nuts and washers. You'll need to be able to swivel the jig so the opening is wider or narrower to accommodate different-sized workpieces.

Setting up a cove cut

Follow the steps outlined in Photos 1 through 3 to determine the proper angle of the parallelogram jig on the saw table. The jig takes the guesswork out of determining how a workpiece must pass over the blade to cut a specific cove curvature.

Step 4, right, outlines the procedure for positioning the first fence on the saw table. In addition to matching the bevel gauge angle, the fence must also be aligned so that the front edge of the blade intersects the front edge of the cove profile you've marked on your workpiece. Clamp a second fence to the saw table to keep the workpiece from shifting away from the first fence when cutting.

Cutting the cove

Lower the blade to a height of about 1/16 in. above the table and make the first cut. Use pushsticks to pass the workpiece over the blade. Raise the blade about 1/16 in. with each pass until you've cut away all the material in the cove area.

How to make cove cuts

1 Draw a curved layout line on the end of your workpiece to mark the cove profile. Raise the blade above the saw table so the teeth at the top of the blade match the highest point of the cove profile.

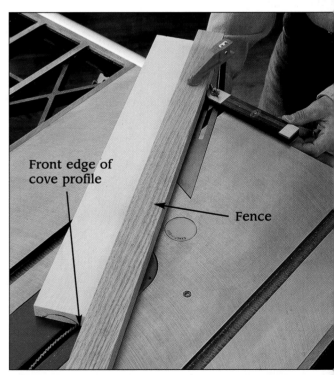

Front edge of cove profile

Fence

4 Select a length of flat stock about 4 ft. long to serve as a fence for guiding the workpiece when you cut the cove. Set the workpiece and fence on the saw table and against the bevel gauge. Shift the fence until the front blade teeth and the front edge of the cove profile intersect. Clamp the fence in place.

2 Adjust the cove parallelogram jig so that the inside edges of the jig match the width of the cove profile. Set the jig on the saw table and over the blade. Turn the whole jig left or right until the inside edges of the jig touch the front and back edges of the blade (See inset photo). In this position, the jig sets the angle you'll need for cutting the cove.

3 Set a bevel gauge to match the angle the parallelogram jig forms with the front edge of the saw table. Be careful not to bump the parallelogram jig out of alignment as you set the angle on the tool.

OPTION: Milling a partial cove

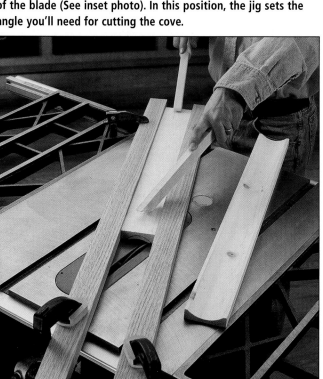

5 Using the workpiece as a spacer, clamp a second fence to the saw table, parallel to the first fence, to create a track for cutting the workpiece. Then cut the cove in a series of shallow passes, increasing the blade height about 1/16 in. with each pass.

Fence

If your cove profile only needs to be a partial curve shape, cut a saw kerf into the fence you clamp to the saw table so the blade is partially buried in the fence. Cut the partial cove profile as you would a full cove, in shallow 1/16-in. passes.

Joinery Techniques

Once your workpieces are cut to size, they'll usually need to be assembled in any of a host of different configurations to form joints. Joints serve three primary functions in a project: They provide flat surfaces on which to apply glue or drive mechanical fasteners; they help bear loads carried by the parts that comprise the joint; and joints allow wood to expand and contract as it is exposed to changes in temperature and humidity.

By design, table saws make excellent, versatile joint-cutting power tools. The saw table, rip fence and miter gauge fence provide plenty of flat support surfaces for holding a workpiece steady as you cut. Add a few clamps, a simple auxiliary wood fence or a handful of shop-made jigs, and nearly any flat workpiece can be safely and accurately moved

through the blade—on edge, on end or on its face. You'll need this degree of cutting control for making joints. In addition, the miter gauge, blade and rip fence settings can be locked into position, so it's easy to duplicate a joint-cutting procedure exactly and quickly on multiple joint parts.

The purpose of the pages that follow is to present a roster of joints that can be made entirely or almost entirely on the table saw. Many more wood joints exist than are covered here, and some of them simply can't be cut on the table saw. However, unless the hallmark of your woodworking is elaborate joinery, the group of joints covered in this chapter should be sufficient to support and beautify virtually any project you set out to build.

Ways to join wood

Glue alone is used for some woodworking techniques, including edge-gluing boards together to form wider panels.

Interlocking joints are fashioned with parts that are cut to link together mechanically. Sometimes they are reinforced with nails or screws to reinforce the glue bond.

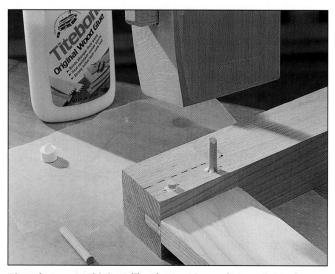

Pinned or pegged joints, like the mortise-and-tenon joint shown here, feature dowels, splines or wedges driven across the joint parts to lock them together.

Joinery Techniques

Wood joinery options are almost too numerous to count—which testifies to a long history of innovations in joint craftsmanship. In almost every instance, you'll find that wood is joined in one of three primary ways, all of which can be accomplished with a table saw: Some boards are attached by butting flat faces, ends or edges together and bonding the joint with glue or mechanical fasteners, such as brads, nails, screws or hinges. Other joints are made by shaping the mating parts into interlocking forms, then strengthening the union of the parts with glue. A third option for constructing strong wood joints is to insert an additional wooden member (such as a spline, biscuit, wedge or dowel) between or through the mating parts. Splines and biscuits serve mainly as alignment aids to keep workpieces from shifting while glue joints are drying, but they also add a degree of structural support to the joint. Dowels and wedges typically pin two workpieces together across the joint, which locks them together.

Which joints you choose for a project should depend largely on the look you are after, the strength you need and the tools you own.

The basics of table saw joinery

Flat, straight (and usually square) cuts should always be your goal when ripping and crosscutting parts to size. This is especially true when woodworking. A ⅛-in. gap between parts is less critical if you are cutting plywood roof sheathing than a ¹⁄₁₆- or ¹⁄₃₂-in. deviation is when making a drawer carcase. The tolerance between these kinds of joint parts is so minimal that parts simply won't fit together unless the mating workpieces are cut precisely.

> **CAUTION:**
> *Some of the photographs you'll see throughout this book show the blade guard and splitter removed. This was done to make the information in the photographs easier to see. To prevent injury, use a working blade guard and a splitter with anti-kickback pawls whenever the type of cut being made allows.*

You'll save time and frustration when preparing parts for making joints if you machine your workpieces so they're as flat, smooth and square as possible.

Once you've flattened and smoothed those surfaces you'll join together, the next step is to lay out your workpieces. It's important to proportion joints so one half of the joint does not compromise the strength of the other half. For instance, when a groove cut in one workpiece must house another workpiece, it shouldn't be cut so deep as to weaken the rest of the grooved workpiece.

Setting up your saw

It should go without saying that a well-tuned saw greatly improves your prospects for cutting nicely tailored joints. The degree of precision you can expect from your saw is somewhat dependent upon the quality of the saw you own, but even inexpensive portable saws are capable of cutting respectable joints if they are tuned up properly. If you've read the chapter in this book on tune-up and maintenance, you'll recall that there are a few very basic relationships you need to pay attention to when tweaking your table saw. Be sure that your rip fence and blade are parallel and your miter gauge is set square to the blade. Since joinery tends to keep you working in close proximity to the blade (many joints require making repeated short crosscuts), it is important that the throatplate is level with the saw table. Cutting joints can produce small waste pieces that can lodge between the blade and the throatplate opening. In these cases, it's a good idea to install a zero-clearance throatplate (See page 33).

Adjusting for precise blade height

Most cuts made with a table saw are *through cuts* that sever a board in two. Crosscuts, rip cuts, miters and bevels are examples of these kinds of through cuts. Cutting joints with interlocking parts, however, frequently will require you to make one or more cuts that extend only partway through the workpiece, called *non-through cuts.* Dadoes, rabbets and slots are examples of this type of cutting operation.

In order to make accurate non-through cuts, you'll need to set blade height precisely to keep the cuts from being too shallow or too deep. A variety of different techniques are used to set blade height. Regardless of the method you choose, always measure off the tooth at the highest point of the blade arc above the saw table. It might be tempting to grab a tape measure to set blade height, but reading off of a flexible tape is difficult because you have to hold the tape in mid-air while you take your reading. A more reliable way to set blade height is to position a try square or combination square on the saw table so it sits perpendicular to the blade, then read blade height off of the graduations on the square. Be sure the throatplate is flush with the surrounding tabletop, or your blade height reading will be inaccurate. To take a reading, position yourself in front of the saw so your line of sight is even with the height of the blade, and look straight-on at the scale next to the blade. Where possible, read off of the scale with the finest increments to get the most accurate reading. If the blade has teeth that bevel to the left and

Options for setting blade height

Combination square. Set a combination square on the saw table and against the blade. Use the rule on the square to set blade height. Select the side of the rule with the finest graduations.

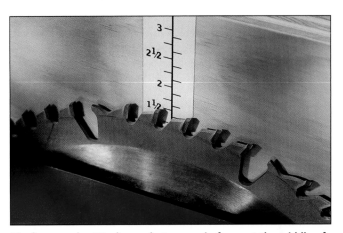

Rip fence scale. Attach a scale to your rip fence at the middle of the blade to serve as a convenient height adjustment reference. Then dial the blade up or down next to the fence to set height.

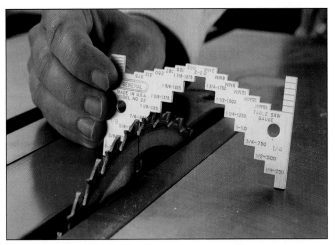

Commercial blade height gauges are stepped off in even increments to take the guesswork out of setting exact blade height. To use the gauge, set it over the blade area and raise the blade until a blade tooth touches the "step" that matches the height you need.

Setting dado blade width

Dado-blade width settings: **Stacked dado blades (left):** Since the outer blades of a stacked dado blade spin in a single orbit like a standard saw blade, simply measure off the outside edges of each outside blade to determine the edges of the saw kerf. If you'll use the same dado-blade setting to cut a number of different workpieces, you can even mark the "inner" and "outer" edges of the dado blade right on the throatplate. **Wobble dadoes (right):** To set the width of a wobble dado blade accurately, dial the blade to roughly the width setting you need and make a test cut on a scrap piece. Adjust the blade if needed, and continue to make test cuts until the kerf width on the scrap matches the correct width. Mark the kerf width of the scrap onto the saw's throatplate.

right, rotate the blade, looking for a chipper-style tooth that is ground flat across. It's easiest to get a reliable reading by measuring off this tooth. Otherwise, set the blade height off the tip of a tooth that bevels toward the square.

A couple other blade setting options are worth considering. A handy way to set blade height without a square is to mark a vertical scale on your rip fence at the high point where it intersects the middle high point of the blade. Mark the scale with increments as fine as you like, but for practicality and accuracy, ⅛- or ¼-in. markings are about as close as you can get measuring off the fence. To use the scale, simply slide the fence next to the blade and raise the blade until the highest tooth intersects the mark corresponding to the blade height you need. Various manufacturers also sell plastic or metal blade height gauges for use with table saw blades or router bits (See photo, previous page). The gauges rest on the saw table and are stepped off in even increments. Just raise the blade until it touches the correct "step" on the gauge.

Choosing a cutting tool

Every joint covered in this chapter can be cut with a standard-kerf combination saw blade. Regardless of the style of joint, building a joint really is just a matter of making a number of through or non-through rip cuts and crosscuts on edges, ends or faces until enough material is removed from two workpieces to make them fit together. The good news about cutting joints with a standard blade is that any saw capable of mak-

ing reliable straight cuts can cut joints—even the smallest benchtop saw.

A standard-kerf saw blade isn't necessarily the most efficient choice for cutting joinery, however. For instance, if the joint you need to cut is a lap joint where the cutaway area is 2 in. wide and not on the end of the board, you'd need to make 16 successive crosscuts, removing ⅛ in. of material at a time to clear away the waste for the joint. Similarly, if the cutaway on the mating piece is also inset on the board, you'll need to make another 16 crosscuts to complete cuts for the joint parts. There's nothing unsafe or incorrect about cutting joints this way, but what a tedious process!

A better way to remove larger amounts of material in fewer passes or even in a single pass is to use a *dado blade* (See pages 54 to 55). Most dado blades have a cutting width capacity of nearly 1 in. That means, at least on shallower cuts and softer woods, you can remove wood at eight times the speed of a standard blade. But to be used effectively, these tools must be kept sharp and in tune. And keep in mind that the greatest mistake most woodworkers make when using dado blades is to try and remove too much material in a single pass. But once you've become comfortable using a dado blade to accomplish your table saw joinery, you'll never want to go back to using a standard blade for these tasks.

Sawing joints safely

Since non-through cuts do not cut a kerf through the workpiece, you'll have to remove your saw's splitter. The trouble with removing the splitter is that on most saws, you'll also have to remove the guard. This leaves you more vulnerable to kickback and to direct contact with the blade. The best solution is to replace your saw's standard guard system with an aftermarket guard. On many aftermarket guards the splitter is removable, so the guard can remain in place for non-through cuts (See pages 134 to 135).

If replacing a guard and splitter isn't within your budget, you can also construct your own guard systems for protecting yourself against kickback. Sometimes simply clamping a piece of stock next to or on top of the workpiece to hold it in place is all the added security you'll need to perform a cut. As you set up your cuts, do whatever you can to limit the blade's ability to lift the workpiece up and propel it back toward you. When the blade is buried within your workpiece, as it is in a non-through cut, every tooth above the saw table has the potential to come in contact with the workpiece at the same time, which is a prime opportunity for kickback.

Using the rip fence and miter gauge together for non-through cuts

Aside from splitter and guard issues, non-through cuts are also unique because in certain circumstances the rip fence and miter gauge can be used in tandem to guide and support workpieces. Remember, crosscuts and rip-cuts that sever a workpiece in two parts create waste pieces that can get trapped between the "triangle" formed by the blade, rip fence and miter gauge. The hazard comes when the skittering, trapped waste piece rubs and catches on the blade teeth on the outfeed side of the blade. In contrast, some non-through cuts do not create waste pieces—only sawdust—so there's no loose projectile produced for the blade to throw back at you. In these situations, the miter gauge serves to support the workpiece as you feed it through the blade, while the rip fence aligns the blade with the layout lines on the workpiece. A number of joint cuts covered in the following pages illustrate how to use the rip fence and miter gauge safely together.

Joint stresses

Wood joints undergo four main types of stress: tension, shear, racking and compression. Each type of joint will vary in its ability to resist failure by one or more of these stresses.

Surface area

Have you ever wondered why some wood joint styles like dovetails or finger joints have interlocking parts? Other than being visually attractive, the parts that mesh together provide a substantial amount of additional surface area on which to apply glue. On properly made joints, glue surface area is directly related to strength. It isn't the only measure of strength, but it is an important one. For strong joints, the more surface area, the better.

Butt joints

Butt joints are the simplest woodworking joints to cut and build. And when used in the right applications, butt joints are quick to assemble and sufficiently strong. A butt joint is formed when two workpieces are butted together on their faces, ends, edges or any combination of these surfaces. Unlike other types of joints, the mating surfaces of a butt joint are left flat and smooth, without any additional machining that would allow the pieces to interlock. Instead, the joint typically is reinforced with only glue, so it gains all of its strength from the glue bond.

Because the mating parts do not interlock, butt joints in woodworking situations are inherently weaker than other styles and are best left for joining parts that don't need to move or support great amounts of weight. Modern woodworking glues form incredibly strong joints—on a properly made joint, the surrounding wood fibers will break before the glue joint fails. But glue alone won't save a butt joint subjected to excessive twisting, pulling or shearing forces. If you choose to use butt joints for building drawers or doors, be sure to reinforce the joint with nails, screws or biscuits where it will be subjected to tension or racking stresses, to keep the joint from pulling apart. Nails, dowels, splines, screws or bolts will strengthen a butt joint that must carry a load, preventing it from failing due to shear.

Butt joints are used for edge-gluing individual

boards together to form wide panels such as tabletops, carcases, workbench and "butcher-block" surfaces and cutting boards. Edge-glued butt joints are stronger than other butt joint configurations because the boards are joined lengthwise, along the grain (called *long-grain*). Long-grain gluing provides plenty of surface area for glue along the joint, and because the wood pores run parallel to the joint instead of across it, the boards can expand and contract evenly across the grain as temperature and humidity fluctuate. Plus, long grain soaks up just enough glue to hold the joint tightly.

A good way to help align long boards in a glue-up is to insert biscuits into the joint. Cut the slots with a biscuit joiner, centering the biscuits across the thickness of the boards.

Another good situation to use butt joints is for face-gluing boards together. This is a common practice for assembling boards into

Right angle butt joint

Butt joints	
STRESS RESISTANCE:	
Tension: Poor	
Compression: Good	
Shear: Poor	
Racking: Poor	
COMMON USES:	
Edge-glued panels; Light-duty carcase, drawer and frame construction; rough framing for construction	

How to cut mated edges for an edge-glued butt joint

1 Lay the two workpieces next to one another in the same orientation in which they'll be fastened. For reference, draw a line or a "V" across the joint.

2 Rip-cut a narrow strip of stock from one of the mating edges. The reference line on the board should be facing up.

thicker blanks used to make project parts such as table legs and columns. When face gluing, run the board faces across a jointer or through a thickness planer to ensure that they are flat.

Face-glued butt joint (lamination)

Cutting butt joints

Sawing parts for butt joints involves making square, smooth rip cuts and cross-cuts. Follow the procedures outlined on pages 56 to 97 for setting up and making these basic cuts.

A handy technique for sawing smooth, tightly fitting edges is to alternate the desired faces of the boards when running them through the saw (See photos, below). If your saw is properly tuned and your blade cuts without leaving noticeable saw marks, you can glue butt joints together without needing to plane or joint the edges further. However, jointing the edges can't hurt

Biscuit-reinforced butt joint

either long-grain or end-grain glue-ups, so run your workpieces over a jointer where possible, or smooth the mating surfaces with a sharp hand plane. Smoothing the mating surfaces minimizes small gaps that can trap air beneath the glue layer.

When you butt the parts together, check the fit of the parts carefully by laying them side by side on a workbench. Any noticeable gaps that run lengthwise along the joint indicate that the saw blade wasn't set perfectly square to the saw table for one or both cuts. Or, one of the work-pieces may have drifted away from the rip fence slightly, result-ing in a wavy cut. You may also have started with a board that isn't straight along its edge. In these situations, you'll need to flatten and square the mating surfaces further before applying glue or clamping up the joint.

Edge-glued butt joint

3 Rip-cut a narrow strip of stock from the mating edge of the other board. This time, the reference lines on the board should be facing down.

4 Test the fit with the boards oriented in the same fashion as they were when you drew the reference line. Flipping one of the boards should result in a tight perpendicular joint, even if the blade and fence are slightly out of square.

How to edge-glue with splines

1 Set the blade height to one-half the width of the spline, plus ⅟₃₂ in. Make a lengthwise kerf cut on each mating edge.

2 Measure your saw blade kerf, then rip splines to that thickness. Test the fit. If necessary, adjust the saw setup and cut new splines—don't try to trim splines that are too thick.

3 Apply wood glue in one of the slots, then insert the spline. Apply glue in the mating slot and slip the mating board over the spline. Draw the workpieces together with clamps. Do not overtighten the clamps.

Splined butt joints

Splines are thin strips of solid wood or plywood inserted into matching slots cut into both members of a joint. On splined butt joints, the slot runs along the joint, centered on the thickness of the mating workpieces. Adding a spline between mating surfaces of a simple butt joint is an easy modification to make and offers several advantages over butt joints bonded with glue alone. First, splines act like dowels or biscuits to help interlock and align members of a joint during glue-up. Cutting spline slots along the length of a butt joint also contributes to a stronger glue joint, since the spline slot more than doubles the surface area for glue. Increasing the gluing area helps strengthen the joint against forces of tension, stress and racking. Plus, the spline acts almost like a tenon, making the joint more resistant to failure caused by shear forces. A spline joint, however, isn't as strong as other two-part interlocking joints that will be covered in this chapter.

Splined edge joint (through)

Cutting spline joints

The width of a spline is typically equal to the thickness of the mating parts, so you'd use a ¾-in.-wide spline for 1× stock. Spline thickness should not exceed one-third the thickness of the mating pieces. For gluing up ¾-in.-thick stock, splines ranging from ⅛- to ¼-in. thick are suitable. Since splines serve primarily as alignment aids, splines wider than ¾ in. do not contribute more strength to the joint. When gluing up boards thicker than ¾ in., a better alternative is to install two splines side by side in the joint.

Splined edge joint (concealed)

To cut a spline slot, install either a standard-kerf saw blade or dado blade in the saw and set the blade height to one-half the spline width plus about 1/32 in. (the extra height allows for excess glue). If using a dado blade, you'll also need to set the cutting width. If you don't own a dado blade but need to cut a spline slot wider than the width of your saw blade, make multiple passes with a standard blade.

Right-angle splined joint

Lay out slot locations on each member of the joint. Splined butt joints are strongest when the splines are centered on the thickness of the mating parts. Then set the rip fence so the saw blade aligns with the layout marks on your workpieces. Cut the slots for the parts. Use a tall fence to support wide workpieces when cutting on-edge, and use a tenoning jig for cutting the ends of long, narrow boards. Install featherboards to hold your workpieces tight against the rip fence when possible.

To make sure the slots on mating boards align, mark the board faces and run the marked faces through the saw in the same orientation.

Cutting splines

To make splines, measure the width of the spline slot carefully to set up the cut. Rip-cut splines from the edge of a board so the splines fall away from the blade on the side opposite the rip fence. If you want to hide the spline ends, cut concealed slots or make the splines from the same wood species as the workpieces. For a decorative highlight, choose wood with contrasting color.

To cut several narrow splines quickly and easily, use a narrow ripping jig (See page 70).

Splined butt joints
Stress resistance:
Tension: Fair
Compression: Good
Shear: Fair
Racking: Fair
Common uses:
Edge-glued panels; "free-floating" cabinet panels; carcase, drawer and frame construction

How to cut a concealed spline joint

1 With your saw unplugged, set up for the cut by raising the saw blade to the cutting depth (usually 3/8 in.), then marking the points of first and last contact with blade onto the saw table. Make a reference mark 1 in. from each end of the workpiece, then clamp a wood block to the saw fence, positioned so the reference marks will align with the appropriate blade contact marks at the start and finish of the cut.

2 Using a featherboard to hold the workpiece against the fence, turn on the saw and carefully lower the workpiece onto the spinning blade. The back end of the workpiece should be butted flush against the start block.

3 Feed the workpiece through the blade, guiding it with a pushstick. When the front end contacts the stopblock, switch off the saw and remove the workpiece once the blade stops spinning.

Rabbet joints

Rabbets (sometimes called *rebates*) are rectangular cuts made along the edge or end of a workpiece to form a tongue. Rabbet joints are made in two styles: In the case of *double rabbet* and *shiplap* joints, a rabbet is cut into the mating ends or edges of both workpieces, and the proportions of the rabbets match one another. This way, the rabbetted parts can be combined so the workpieces form a right angle (double rabbet) or a flat plane (shiplap). A second rabbet joint style, called an *overlap rabbet,* involves cutting a deep rabbet in one workpiece so it overlaps the square end or edge of a mating workpiece.

Rabbet joints are a better alternative to butt joints for building boxes and carcases because the joints partially interlock. You'll commonly see double rabbets and overlap rabbets used in bookcase construction to conceal the ends and edges of the back and top panels. Depending upon how the joints are arranged, both of these rabbet joint types can conceal most of the end grain. Double and overlapping rabbet joints typically are bonded with glue and reinforced with brads or nails.

Shiplap joints are superior to edge-glued butt joints when gluing up panels because the "stepped" pattern of the joint lends one-third more surface area for gluing, creating a stronger joint. When the rabbets are cut accurately, a shiplap self-aligns the workpiece faces and resists shifting during glue-up.

Double rabbet

Cutting with a standard blade

Cutting rabbets with a standard-kerf saw blade involves cutting the cheeks with one saw set up, then trimming the shoulders in a second operation. For double and shiplap rabbet joints, mark cheek and shoulder layout lines on both workpieces, checking the rabbet layouts against one another to be sure the proportions will match. It doesn't matter which cut you make first—cheeks or shoulders—but it is most efficient to make like cuts on all workpieces before you change fence or blade settings to make the second set of cuts. Also, be sure that the waste piece is on the side of the blade opposite the fence so it does not become trapped between the fence and the blade when it falls free.

To make cheek cuts, you'll need to stand workpieces on edge or end against the rip fence. Install a tall fence for rabbeting the edges of wide workpieces, and use a tenoning jig to support workpieces with cheek cuts on the board ends. When setting the distance from the rip fence to the blade, be careful that the blade will cut inside the waste area of the rabbet, rather than into the tongue of the rabbet (See photo, next page). Set the blade height so the teeth just touch your shoulder layout marks. Make a test cut on scrap to check your fence and blade settings.

For rabbets that follow the edge of a workpiece, cut the shoulders using the rip fence as a guide. Rabbet shoulders cut into the end of a board should be cut with the miter gauge as a guide. Be sure to reset blade height for cutting shoulders on overlap rabbet joints, because the shoulders are shorter than the cheeks.

Overlap rabbet

Shiplap rabbet

Double-rabbet joints
STRESS RESISTANCE:
Tension: Fair
Compression: Good
Shear: Good
Racking: Fair
COMMON USES:
Light-duty drawer construction; carcases & boxes; edge-glued panels

Cutting with a dado blade

Dado blades make quick work of cutting rabbets, because the blade cuts the cheek and shoulder in one pass. Regardless of the dimensions of the rabbet, orient your workpieces to lie facedown on the saw table when you make rabbet cuts with a dado blade. The width of the dado will set the height of the rabbet cheek, and the height of the blade will determine the depth of the shoulder. If the depth of the shoulders exceeds the maximum height of the dado blade, you'll have to make the cheek and shoulder cuts with another saw, such as a band saw or a reciprocating saw.

Install a sacrificial wood fence on the rip fence and set the dado blade to cut wider than needed to cut the rabbet. Raise the dado into the sacrificial fence so part of the blade will be shrouded by the sacrificial fence. Set the blade height and fence distance from the blade to match the cheek and shoulders of your rabbet. For rabbets that follow the edge of a workpiece, make the cut by guiding the workpiece along the rip fence and over the dado.

Dado blades create more resistance against a workpiece than a standard saw blade, and the resistance increases the more material you remove in one pass. Clamp a scrap hold-down block or featherboard above the workpiece to help hold the workpiece against the saw table as you cut with a dado blade.

When cutting a rabbet along the end of a workpiece that's narrower than about 8 in., use the miter gauge to support the workpiece from behind as you feed it over the blade. It is safer to use the miter gauge in tandem with the rip fence in this instance, rather than simply pushing the workpiece through by hand, because the miter gauge provides broader support and keeps the workpiece from shifting. Without the miter gauge, you would be forced to run the narrow edge of the work-piece tight against the fence.

How to cut a rabbet with a standard blade

1 Draw layout lines for the rabbet on the workpiece. Set the blade height and ripping width to the dimensions of the rabbet, then make the cheek cut. Use a featherboard to hold the workpiece against the fence. To prevent the waste piece from becoming trapped in the throat opening, use a zero-clearance throat-plate (See page 33).

2 With the rip fence positioned so the waste piece will be on the outside of the blade, make the shoulder cut. Use a push pad to guide the workpiece over the blade.

How to cut a rabbet with a dado blade set

Hold-down

Sacrificial fence

Featherboard

A dado blade can cut shallow rabbets in a single pass. If the rabbet is deeper than 3/8 in. or the workpiece is hardwood, make the cut in multiple passes. Attach a sacrificial wood fence to the rip fence. Set the fence position and cutting depth, then make the cut. Use a hold-down, featherboard and push-stick to guide the workpiece.

How to cut a bare-faced tongue-&-dado joint

1 Lay out and cut the dado. We used a dado blade to cut the ¼-in.-wide dado for the drawer back shown above. We used the rip fence as a stopblock to index the cut and guided the workpiece with the miter gauge (because no through cut is being made there is no risk of the waste piece binding).

2 Make the cheek cut for the rabbet. We used a shop-made tenoning jig (See pages 156 to 157) to secure the workpiece as we made the cut.

Rabbet-&-dado joints

Rabbet-and-dado joints combine the enhanced gluing area of a rabbet with the interlocking characteristics of a dado or groove to form joints that are very resistant to failure from racking or shear. Rabbet and dado joints take two forms, depending on their intended purpose. One style features a rabbet with a tongue half the thickness of the workpiece that fits into a matching dado or groove. This joint is used commonly to fasten shelves to upright standards, such as bookcases. The ends of the shelves receive the rabbets, while the standards are dadoed. Another less common use of this joint is for frame and panel doors—the rabbet is cut around the four edges of the panel and the dado (actually a groove in this case) is centered around the inside edges of the frame.

Rabbet-&-dado joint

The panel side with the rabbet tongues faces out, which leaves a decorative "reveal" between the front of the frame and the panel. The advantage to this frame-and-panel style is that the panel can set back from the front face of the frame without needing to be beveled or planed in order to fit in the narrow dado.

A second form of rabbet-and-dado joint, often called the "bare-faced" tongue and dado, features a thin rabbet tongue that fits into a ¼-in.-deep dado in the face of the mating workpiece. The tongue can be as thin as ⅛ in. but should not exceed one-fourth the thickness of the workpiece. This joint is primarily used to form cor-

Rabbet-&-dado joints
STRESS RESISTANCE:
Tension: Fair
Compression: Good
Shear: Good
Racking: Good
COMMON USES:
Drawer and bookshelf construction; carcases; boxes

3 Finish the rabbet by making the shoulder cut to remove the waste from the rabbet area. A miter gauge with an auxiliary fence is being used to guide the cut.

4 Assemble the joint. For most purposes, glue alone will provide adequate reinforcement.

ner joints in drawers. Rabbets are cut along the ends of the drawer front or back, and dadoes are cut in the drawer sides. Since drawer joints are located either in or close to the ends of the drawer parts, the thin tongue side of the joint faces into the drawer. Positioning the tongue further into the drawer sides keeps the tongue from weakening the short-grain material between the tongue and the ends of the drawer sides.

Bare-faced tongue & dado

Cutting rabbet-and-dado joints

Shelf-style rabbet-and-dado joints with thick rabbet tongues can be cut with a standard-kerf saw blade. The rabbet-half of the joint is cut using the same two-step process as was described for cutting rabbet joints with a standard saw blade (See page 109). However, cutting the dado will require several passes with a standard blade to reach the final dado width. For this reason, it's more efficient to cut these joints with a dado blade. Cut the rabbets first, then size the dadoes to match. Dadoes running across the grain should be cut using the miter gauge as a guide. If the dado runs lengthwise and with the grain (called a groove), cut it by running the workpiece along the rip fence.

"Bare-faced" tongue-and-dado joints also can be cut with a dado blade when the thickness of the tongue is equal to or exceeds the minimum width setting of the dado blade (usually $3/16$ in.). Use a standard saw blade with a $1/8$-in. kerf for cutting joints with thinner tongues. Here's how: Mark the dado-side workpieces and set the blade height to $1/4$ in. Cut the dadoes by feeding the workpieces over the blade and against the rip fence. Support workpieces from behind with the miter gauge if sawing across the grain. Next, cut the rabbet tongues in the other workpieces, standing them on-end against a tenoning jig. Since you'll be cutting with the blade only $1/8$ in. from the fence, attach an auxiliary fence to the rip fence and install a zero-clearance throatplate. Lower the blade about $1/32$ in. from the setting used to cut the dadoes. Once you've made the cheek cuts for the rabbet tongue, lay the workpiece flat on the saw table to cut the rabbet shoulder.

Tongue-&-groove joints

Tongue-and-groove joints combine a number of important features to create a strong, easy-to-build alternative to butt or rabbet-and-dado joints. NOTE: *If the groove is cut across the width of a board, the joint is properly known as a tongue-and-dado. Tongue-and-groove joints run along the grain.*

Tongue-&-dado joint

Both joint types are fashioned by cutting a centered tongue in the edge or end of one board that fits into a centered dado or groove on the mating workpiece. As with splined butt joints, the tongue helps align parts during glue-up. By centering the tongue and fitting it into a centered dado or groove, the shoulders on the tongue side of the joint completely hide the slot made by the dado or groove—a real advantage for concealing the slot-side of the joint. The tongue is cut to one-third the thickness of the workpieces, so it strengthens the joint against racking stresses. Centering the tongue along the joint also adds to the overall surface area of the joint.

These centered tongue joints find their way into a variety of different panel and carcase applications. Tongue-and-groove joints are often used to form cabinet back panels, and the pieces are assembled without glue. This way, the panel can expand and contract freely, and the tongues hide gaps that would otherwise show if the parts were merely butted together. Tongue-and-groove or tongue-and-dado joints also are used to build frame-and-panel doors and in drawer carcase construction, but neither of these applications produce the strongest door or drawer joints possible. A better alternative for drawers is the finger joint (See page 124) or the double-dado joint (See page 115). Mortise-and-tenon joints form the strongest frames (See page 120).

Cutting centered tongue joints

Cutting tongue-and-groove or tongue-and-dado joints is a three-step process. You'll first cut the groove or dado along the edge, end or face of one workpiece, then make two identical rabbets along the edge or end of the mating workpiece to form the tongue. It doesn't matter whether you cut the slot first and then the tongue or the other way around, but accuracy is important either way to ensure that the parts fit together snugly without binding. These joints can be cut most efficiently with a dado blade, but you could also use a standard saw blade following the multiple-step process for cutting rabbets and dadoes described on page 109.

Tongue-&-groove joint

To cut the slot, mark the dimensions of the dado or groove onto the face, end or edge of the workpiece. Slot width should equal one-third the thickness of the tongued workpiece. If the slot will be cut into the face of a board, make its depth equal to half the board's thickness. Tongues that run along ends or edges are typically ½ in. long, so set end and edge slots to this depth. Attach a sacrificial wood fence to your rip fence (you'll need it for cutting the tongue) and set the width and height of the dado according to your layout dimensions. Cut the slot in one pass. Use a tenoning jig to support workpieces when cutting grooves that run along the narrow end of a workpiece. For grooves cut along one of the long edges of a workpiece, be sure the sacrificial wood fence is tall enough to provide adequate support as you slide the workpiece along the fence and over the blade. Hold the work snugly against the fence with a featherboard. Use the miter gauge in conjunction with the rip fence when cutting dadoes across the face of a workpiece.

You'll want to cut the tongue slightly shorter than the slot depth so the shoulders of the joint will seat tightly against the slotted workpiece. To account for a shorter tongue, lower the dado blade ½2 to ¼6 in. from the setting you used to cut the slot. Reset the dado width so it's wider than the final tongue width (a dado-blade width of ½ in. is sufficient for cutting the rabbets for tongues in 1× stock). Set the sacrificial rip fence over the dado blade so the exposed area of the blade matches the shoulder width of the tongue (¼ in. for tongues in 1× stock).

Mark the tongue layout on

Tongue-&-groove/dado joints		
STRESS RESISTANCE:		
Tension: Good		
Compression: Good		
Shear: Good		
Racking: Good		
COMMON USES:		
Shelving; solid-wood flooring and paneling; edge-glued or "floating" panels; "breadboard"-style edges and ends for tabletops; drawer carcases; frame-and-panel doors		

How to make a tongue-&-groove joint

Check tongue setting by cutting test board before cutting actual workpiece

1 Cut a groove in the edge of one mating board, using a dado blade or by making multiple passes over a single blade. The groove should be one-third the thickness of the workpiece.

2 On the uncut mating board, remove the waste wood on one side of the tongue area. Any rabbet-cutting technique may be used with either a standard blade or a dado blade.

4 Apply wood glue in the groove, then insert the tongue. The tongue should fit fully in the groove.

3 Flip the workpiece and remove the waste on the other side of the tongue.

both ends or edges of a scrap piece that matches the thickness of the actual workpiece. This way, you can test the fit of the tongue in the slot you've already cut and make adjustments to the dado setup before committing to your final workpiece. To machine the tongue, cut one rabbet along the edge or end of the scrap, flip the board end-for-end (or edge-for-edge) and cut the second rabbet. Support the rabbet cuts appropriately for the specific joint you are building,

using tenoning jigs, tall rip fences, or the miter gauge. If the resulting tongue is too long and holds the joint apart, correct the problem by lowering the dado blade slightly and retest on fresh scrap. Reset the fence forward to cut a thicker tongue or back to trim the tongue thinner. Remember, even a slight adjustment will magnify the changes to a tongue, since you are essentially adding or subtracting thickness by duplicating the same cut on each side of the tongue. Make additional test cuts on scrap until you achieve a good tongue-and-slot fit, then cut your workpieces.

Housed dado joints

Housed dadoes are a quick alternative to cutting either rabbet-and-dado or centered tongue joints when attaching shelves to uprights. To construct the joint, you simply cut a dado that matches the full thickness of the mating board (typically, the shelf). Shelves built with housed dadoes have good shear resistance, but the longer the shelf, the more likely it will twist out of the dado if it should bow. In situations where appearance is not important, reinforce the glue joint by screwing or nailing through the dado and into the housed board. This will also make the joint more resistant to failure from tension stresses. If appearance matters, conceal the finished joint with iron-on veneer tape or solid-wood edging.

Housed dado joint

Cutting a housed dado

The best blade for cutting housed dadoes is a dado blade. When cutting the dadoes, back up the cuts with an auxiliary fence attached to the miter gauge. Otherwise, the dado blade could tear out material on the back side of the workpiece. Lay out the dadoes so the dado depth does not exceed one-half the thickness of the workpiece. Make test cuts in scrap first to check the fit of the parts.

A good practice when cutting housed dadoes for shelving is to cut the dadoes across both shelf standards simultaneously. Do this by cutting dadoes across one workpiece, then ripping the workpiece in half lengthwise to form two identical shelf standards. This way, when you assemble the shelving unit, the shelves will line up perfectly and parallel with one another between the standards.

Housed dado joints
STRESS RESISTANCE:
Tension: Fair
Compression: Good
Shear: Good
Racking: Good
COMMON USES:
Attaching shelving to carcases and drawer backs to sides

Tips for cutting housed dadoes

Metal or paper shims

Find the right width. If you are using a stacked dado blade to cut a housed dado, be sure the dado width is precise so the housed piece will fit tightly into the dado. Experiment with different groupings of chippers and shims until the exact cutting width is attained.

Guaranteed shelf alignment. When cutting housed dadoes in bookshelf standards, cut the dadoes across a wide workpiece, then rip the workpiece in half to create two identical standards.

Blind dado joints

Blind dado joints have the same structural characteristics as housed dadoes, but the dado stops short of running completely through to the front of the workpiece. The joint is concealed on the finished side without the need for veneer tape or wood edging. A corner of the housed member of the joint is notched so it fits into the end of the dado, but it still allows the part to extend all the way to the finished side of the assembly.

Cutting a blind dado

Stopping a dado cut on a table saw at a specific point involves establishing a reference point on the saw table or fence to mark where the cut should end on the workpiece. You could set this reference by marking on a piece of tape, but this method requires you to stop the cut by visually aligning the edge of the workpiece with the marker. A more accurate and foolproof method is to clamp a stopblock to the saw table. This way, the reference marker is also a physical barrier to keep you from accidentally cutting too far.

To set up the stopblock for cutting blind dadoes, set your workpiece against the miter fence and slide the workpiece forward until the leading edge of the board touches the dado-blade teeth on the infeed side of the blade. Determine the length of the dado cut by measuring across the width of your workpiece and subtracting the amount by which you wish to stop the dado short of the workpiece edge. Without moving the workpiece, measure this distance, starting from where the workpiece touches the blade. Clamp a stopblock in place at this point. Be sure to clamp the stopblock firmly to the saw table to keep it from shifting during the cut, especially if you are making multiple matching cuts on your workpieces.

(Continued next page.)

Blind dado joint

Blind dado joints	
STRESS RESISTANCE:	
Tension:	Fair
Compression:	Good
Shear:	Good
Racking:	Good
COMMON USES:	
Shelf support	

Double-dado joints

Double-dado joints are a hybrid cousin of the tongue-and-groove joint, but they can be a little befuddling to the eye when you study how the parts fit together. Unlike standard tongue-and-groove joints, double dadoes actually have a tongue on each member of the joint, rather than a tongue on one part that fits into a dado or groove on the other part. Notice that the tongues on both joint parts are off center and the same length. When you fit the joint together, the tongues fit into dadoes in the opposite workpiece.

By virtue of their interlocking configuration, double dadoes are resistant to nearly all joint stresses and provide a large surface area in and around the tongues and grooves for glue. They are also a good choice for applications where exposed end grain is undesirable. These joints could be used for carcase construction, but you'll find them most commonly reinforcing drawer frames. The side of the joint that conceals the end grain of the other joint part becomes the front of the drawer. This way, both the interlocking tongues and the glue bond strengthen the joint against stresses associated with opening and closing the drawer.

Double-dado joint

Double-dado joints	
STRESS RESISTANCE:	
Tension:	Fair
Compression:	Good
Shear:	Good
Racking:	Good
COMMON USES:	
Drawer construction	

Cutting double-dado joints

The best procedure for cutting double dadoes is to cut the "drawer side" dado first to establish the thickness and length of one tongue, then cut the dado on the end of the "drawer front" and trim the tongue in one or more passes until the tongues and dadoes interlock and the drawer side fits fully into the drawer front.

(Continued on page 117.)

Blind dado joints (continued)

If you've calculated correctly, the dado cut should terminate exactly where you want when you make an initial cut on a scrap piece. To cut closer to the edge of the board, adjust the stopblock so it's closer to the blade. To stop the cut farther from the edge of the workpiece, adjust the stopblock so it's farther from the blade. Once you've cut the dadoes, square up the ends of the stopped cuts with a chisel.

Scribe layout lines for the notches on the corners of the workpieces (usually shelves) that will be housed in the dadoes. The dimensions of the notches should match the depth of the dadoes and the distance by which the dadoes stop short of the front edge of the workpiece. Cut the notches by standing the shelves on edge against the miter gauge and a tall auxiliary miter fence. Inset the dado blade in a sacrificial rip fence so the width of the exposed blade and its height above the saw table match the layout lines of the "shelf" notches. Set the end of each shelf against the rip fence and use the miter gauge to support the workpiece as you feed it through the blade.

How to cut a blind dado joint

First blade contact

Stopblock

1 Use a rule or tape measure to position a stop block at the end of the cut, allowing for the length of the workpiece.

Fence

Hold-down

Workpiece

Stopblock

2 With a fence attached to your miter gauge, clamp a hold-down over the back of the workpiece. Make the cut.

3 Clean out and square off the stopped end of the blind dado with a sharp chisel (preferably, the same width as the dado).

Sacrificial fence

4 Notch the un-dadoed workpiece (typically, a shelf) at both ends to fit around the front edges of the dadoed workpieces. A dado blade that's partially recessed into a sacrificial fence is perfect for cutting notches.

Double-dado joints (continued)

If two drawer parts are each ¾ in. thick, set your dado blade to ¼ in. wide and ⅜ in. cutting depth. Set the rip fence ¼ in. from the blade. Cut the drawer side dado on scrap stock first to check your setup. Since you are cutting the dado on a narrow end of the board, back up the cut with an auxiliary fence attached to the miter gauge. Adjust the setup as necessary and cut the drawer side dado in the actual workpiece. If you plan to use the same joint all around a drawer, cut the other three dadoes in the two drawer sides at this time. NOTE: *Double dadoes are usually cut on the drawer front only. The drawer back, which is subjected to less stress, is held in place with housed dadoes.*

Cut the dadoes in both ends of the drawer front by clamping the drawer front on-end in a tenoning jig. Set the depth of the dado to match the thickness of the drawer side. Trim the inside tongues on the drawer front to length until the drawer side fits completely into the drawer front (See Step 3, below). To trim the tongues, lower the dado blade so it just trims off the tongue without cutting into the other tongue.

How to cut a double dado joint

1 (above) Cut the first dado in one of the "drawer side" workpieces using a dado blade or by making multiple passes with a standard saw blade.

2 (right) Use a tenoning jig to stabilize the "drawer front" workpiece as you cut a dado in the ends of the board.

3 Trim off the top, inside face of the "drawer front" workpiece to create a short tongue that will fit into each dado in the drawer sides.

Drawer front

Drawer side

4 Apply glue into the bottom of each dado and assemble the joint.

Lap joints

Lap joints combine the interlocking characteristics of rabbets and dadoes in a number of different configurations to join two boards face to face. Lap joints are a better alternative to butt joints for frame construction, because laps offer much more gluing area and the pieces actually interlock mechanically. Usually, the thickness of both parts of a lap joint are equal, and the pieces fit together so that both faces of each joint part line up with one another. In order to do this, the overlapping dadoes or rabbet tongues are as large as the mating piece is wide.

Several lap joint styles can be cut entirely on the table saw: corner half-laps, "T" half-laps, cross half-laps, full laps, angled half-laps and bridle joints. "Half-lap" joints get their name because the dadoes or rabbets cut for the joint extend half the thickness of each workpiece. Since the interlocking portions of half-lap joints match, the same blade setup can be used for cuts on both workpieces, which reduces the number of setups needed to cut the joint.

The procedures for cutting lap joints on a table saw are similar, regardless of the specific joint. Corner half-laps consist of two wide rabbets cut across the faces of two workpieces at the board ends. The

cheek portion of each rabbet matches the width of the opposite workpiece. "T" half-laps fasten the end of one board with a wide rabbet to the midsection of another board that's fitted with a matching dado. Full lap joints resemble "T" half-laps, but the dado is actually deep enough to house the full thickness of the board joined on end, so it needs no rabbet. "T" half-laps, cross half-laps and angled half-laps all are made by cutting two wide dadoes into the joint members— either on the faces or edges—then interlocking the dadoes.

Cutting lap joints

Aside from their larger size, the rabbets and dadoes of lap joints are cut just like any other rabbet or dado. Whatever blade you choose,

Lap joints
STRESS RESISTANCE:
Tension: Fair to Good
Compression: Fair to Good
Shear: Fair to Good
Racking: Fair
COMMON USES:
Frame & face frame construction; furniture leg stretchers

Tips for cutting lap joints

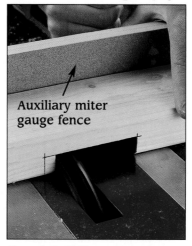

Auxiliary miter gauge fence

Use a dado blade to remove waste material quickly from notches used in lap joinery.

Cut angled half-laps by adjusting the protractor head on the miter gauge. Note the sandpaper adhered to the auxiliary miter gauge fence for extra grip on the board.

How to cut the tongue for a half-lap joint

"T" half-lap

Cross half-lap

you'll need to make multiple passes to cut these rabbets and dadoes. For most efficient cutting, it makes sense to use a dado blade so you can remove more material with each pass. A dado blade is also the right choice for long or unwieldy workpieces. In these instances, cut the rabbets or dadoes in multiple passes with the workpiece lying facedown on the saw table. Be sure to guide only manageably sized workpieces in a tenoning jig whenever you need to cut rabbets with the workpiece standing on end.

1 We used a crosscut sled (See page 85) to guide the workpiece when making the initial shoulder cuts for the tongue portion of this half-lap member. Cut halfway through the thickness of the board at a cutting width that matches the width of the mating workpiece (See *Tip*, next photo).

TIP: Use the workpiece as a reference for setting up the width of cut of the mating tongue.

2 Use a tenoning jig to stabilize your workpiece when trimming away the waste in the cheek area of the tongue.

Mortise-&-tenon joints

Mortise-and-tenon joints are traditional joints for fine furnituremaking. You won't find mortise-and-tenon joints in many mass-produced pieces of furniture or cabinets these days, especially with modern quick fastening options like wood biscuits and pocket screws increasing in popularity. But whenever strength and stress resistance are critical and quality is a concern, you'll likely find a mortise-and-tenon joint.

Mortise-and-tenon joints take full advantage of those factors that contribute most to joint strength: namely, large gluing surface area and parts that interlock. Have a look at the various types of mortise-and-tenon joints illustrated on this page. You'll see that tenons have from two to four cheeks and shoulders, and all of these cheek and shoulder faces contribute surfaces for glue. As a rule of thumb, tenons are usually one-third the thickness of the workpiece and up to 3 in. long. These proportions maximize the shear strength of the tenon without compromising the strength of the mortise walls on the mating workpiece. A properly constructed mortise-and-tenon interlocks snugly without binding, just loose enough to permit a thin, even glue bond along the full joint.

Cutting mortise-and-tenon joints

Only one style of mortise-and-tenon joint, the *open style*, can be cut entirely on the table saw. The mortise is situated on the end of the workpiece, and one end of the mortise is open, so the mortise slot can be cut on the table saw if the workpiece is fed through the blade with the help of a tenoning jig. The tenon tongue fits into the open mortise on the edge or end of the mortise workpiece, so the joint resembles an elongated tongue-and-groove. Other mortise-and-tenon joint types all incorporate a mortise that is hollowed out from the workpiece. These mortises must be excavated with a mortising chisel, drill bit in a drill press or right-angle drilling jig, plunge router or dedicated mortising machine with special hollow chiseling bits.

The process for cutting tenons on a table saw is straightforward, simple and pos-

Through mortise-&-tenon

sible with either a standard saw blade or a dado blade. Which blade you choose depends mainly on the number of tenons you need to cut and the proportions of the workpiece.

Cheek and shoulder cuts can be made with a standard saw blade in two ways: First, you can cut the tenon with the workpiece face lying on the saw table by making multiple, side-by-side shallow passes to clear away one cheek at a time. Clamp a stopblock to the miter gauge to start the cheek cuts at the shoulders, and form each cheek by working toward the end of the workpiece. Then, flip the workpiece to the opposite face, cut the second shoulder and proceed with cutting the second cheek. If the tenon has four cheeks and shoulders, stand the workpiece on edge against the miter gauge to cut the narrow cheeks. You may need to change the blade height for cutting the narrow cheeks, but the stopblock position doesn't change.

Another method for cutting tenons with a standard blade is to cut each cheek in one pass with the workpiece standing on-end against the tenoning jig. Set the blade height so the tips of the teeth cut to the

Open mortise-&-tenon

Haunched mortise-&-tenon

Wedged mortise-&-tenon

Mortise-&-tenon joints
Stress resistance:
Tension: Good
Compression: Good
Shear: Good
Racking: Good
Common uses:
Frame, face frame and door construction; joining table aprons and chair rails to legs

shoulder line, and be sure to account for the thickness of the blade when setting up the cuts. Set the blade so it cuts on the waste side of the tenon layout line to keep from cutting into the tenon. If the tenon has four shoulders and cheeks, cut the narrow edges by clamping the workpiece on-end to a miter gauge outfitted with a tall auxiliary fence. Once you've cut all the cheeks, trim away the remaining waste by cutting the shoulders with the workpiece facedown or

CAUTION:
Some of the photographs you'll see throughout this book show the blade guard and splitter removed. This was done to make the information in the photographs easier to see. To prevent injury, use a working blade guard and a splitter with anti-kickback pawls whenever the type of cut being made allows.

How to cut tenons

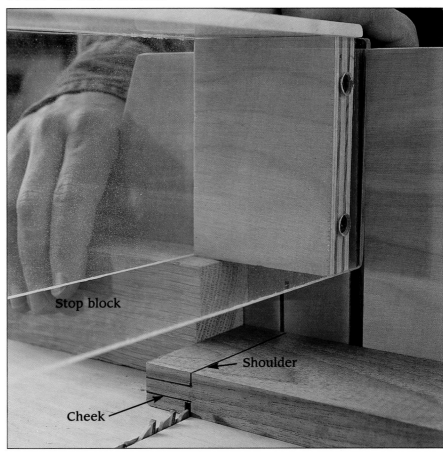

Stop block

Shoulder

Cheek

1 Lay out cut lines for the tenon on the end of your workpiece. Use a stop block to index the shoulder cuts. For small workpieces, use a crosscut sled (page 85) if you have one.

2 Make additional crosscuts away from the shoulder of the tenon, removing waste wood. This part of the cut can get repetitive; take care to maintain your focus.

3 Smooth the tenon cheeks with a sharp wood chisel.

How to cut a haunched tenon

1 When making heavy-duty frames, such as for building doors, extra twist resistance is always desirable. The haunched mortise-and-tenon is significantly more rigid than the blind mortise-and-tenon joint. Start cutting the tenons as with any other tenon: here, a dado blade is being used to "hog out" the waste wood.

2 Clamp the workpiece on-edge to your miter gauge auxiliary fence. Trim the bottom of the tenon to size.

3 Cut the haunched portion of the tenon, usually starting about ¾ in. from the shoulder. Cut the mortise into the mating workpiece, using the haunched tenon as a template for outlining the cut.

on-edge against the miter gauge. Be sure to reset the blade height carefully so you trim just to the saw kerfs cut for the cheeks. Use a stop-block clamped to the miter gauge to index the shoulder cuts.

A dado blade will cut tenon cheeks and shoulders more quickly because it removes more material with each pass. Use the same multiple-pass technique as you would with a single blade to cut tenons with the workpiece flat on the saw table. Use a stopblock to establish the shoulder cuts, and make these cuts first. You can also stand the workpiece on end to cut a cheek and shoulder in one pass with a dado blade, but your depth of cut may be limited if you are using an 8-in.-dia. dado blade in your 10-in. table saw.

By all means clamp your workpiece securely to the tenoning jig if you are running a workpiece on-end through a dado blade raised high above the saw table. Also slow down your feed rate. The dado blade will produce considerably more resistance on the workpiece as you make the cut because it is removing much more wood.

How to cut an open mortise-&-tenon jont

1 (left) Clamp the workpiece to a tenoning jig and cut the tenon cheeks.

2 (above) Trim off the waste to create the shoulders. Use your miter gauge and auxiliary fence to feed the workpiece into the blade, indexing the cuts with a stopblock.

3 (left) Cut a through-mortise using the same setup you used to cut the tenon cheeks. The mortise should be equal in thickness and depth to the tenon, and centered on the workpiece.

4 (above) Test the fit and adjust the tenon thickness, if necessary, by sanding. Apply glue to the mortise and assemble the joint. If the tenon is too long, plane or sand it flush after the glue sets.

Finger joints

Finger joints (sometimes called *box joints*) typically are made on a table saw with a dado-blade set and a jig—an auxiliary board screwed or clamped to the miter gauge. When joining parts of equal thickness, a finger joint is a good choice because it's strong and effective. Like a dovetail, the finger joint is visible after it's assembled—a plus if you like to show off your handiwork (and what woodworker doesn't?). Unlike dovetail pins, finger joint pins are straight, so it's an easier joint to make than a dovetail, although it's not as strong.

To make accurate finger joints, first rip-cut and cross-cut the parts to size. Cut some test slots in waste pieces with the dado blade and check the fit of an actual workpiece in the slot. The workpiece should fit snugly without having to pound it in.

Finger joints
STRESS RESISTANCE:
Tension: Good
Compression: Good
Shear: Good
Racking: Good
COMMON USES:
Corners on boxes and chests

How to cut finger joints

1 Install a dado-blade set and throatplate in your table saw. Set the cutting width of the dado blade to equal the thickness of the finger pins to be cut. Raise the blade set to cut the full depth of the pins. Clamp an auxiliary fence board to your table saw miter gauge. The board should be about 6 in. wide and at least 18 in. long. Make a pass of the auxiliary fence over the blade, then cut a strip of hardwood to use as a pin to fit in the slot, and glue it into the fence slot.

4 Reposition the workpiece by placing the slot you just cut over the pin space, then make the next cut. Continue in this manner until all the joints in that board are cut. Flip the board end-for-end and cut the fingers on the other end of the board the same way.

2 Reset the auxiliary fence by moving it a distance equal to the thickness of one pin to the outside edge of the dado blade. Reclamp or screw the fence to the miter gauge.

3 With the pin spacer inserted in the fence slot and the fence in position, butt the first workpiece against the strip and make the first pass. You can hold the workpiece in place by hand or clamp it to make the cut. After the workpiece and fence clear the blade, shut off the saw and back the workpiece off.

5 To cut the joints in the mating boards, fit the last notch you cut in the first piece over the pin, then butt the mating piece against the first piece, creating a one-notch offset. Make the first pass on the mating piece. Now remove the first piece, butt the notch in the mating piece against the pin and make the second pass. Continue until all the joints are cut in one end, then flip the board end-for-end and repeat.

6 When all the joints are cut, the pieces are ready for assembly. Glue the joints and clamp them together with wood cauls offset from the joints to allow the joints to close.

Splined miter joints

Just as splines can help align and reinforce butt joints, they can also improve the strength and appearance of miter joints and bevel joints. When reinforcing miter joints, the spline is often cut from a contrasting wood to the members of the joint, which also adds a decorative accent to the joint. But the spline can also be made of the same wood as the rest of the frame so it blends in with the joint.

When splines are used to reinforce a bevel joint, the advantages are entirely structural. The spline helps line up the joint corners during glue-up and reinforces the joint once the glue dries. The spline is visible from the top and bottom edges of the workpieces, but at least one set of these edges is typically covered by a structure above, such as a base cabinet over a beveled toe-kick, so the spline is essentially hidden.

Cutting splined miter joints

Reinforcing a miter joint with splines involves cutting shallow slots into the mitered end of the workpiece in one of two ways. In the case of *splined miter joints,* a shallow kerf cut is made across the width of each workpiece, along the mitered end. When the joint is assembled, the spline fits evenly between the workpieces and across the full width of the joint. Consequently, the spline is exposed on both the inside and outside corners of the joint. When splines are used in ¾-in.-thick frame members, the spline is typically ⅛ in. thick and ¾ in. wide. The safest way to cut these splines is to clamp the workpiece on-end against a simple scrap plywood jig supported from behind by a backer board fastened at a 45° angle to the plywood (See photo, page 129). Attach a tall auxiliary fence to the saw's rip fence. Set the blade height to ⅜ in. and center the blade on the width of the workpiece. Clamp the workpiece in the jig so the mitered end is flat

Splined miter joint

against the saw table. Slide the jig along the fence to cut each spline slot.

A second option for splining a miter joint is to cut a spline slot through the outside corner of the miter joint, perpendicular to the 45° line formed by the joint parts, called a *feather joint.* You'll need to build a spline-cutting jig to cut these slots, since neither long edge of the mitered workpieces touches the saw table. (For plans on building a spline-cutting jig, see pages 152 to 153).

Most spline-cutting jigs consist of a V-shaped cradle to support the mitered parts, with a backer board attached to the cradle to provide a clamping surface. Some splining jigs ride in the saw's miter slots, but most ride against the saw fence. It's a good idea to glue up the miters and allow the glue to dry before cutting the splines. This ensures that the frame parts stay aligned in the jig while you make the spline cut (but this isn't a necessity, especially if you clamp the workpieces in place firmly in the jig).

Splined bevel joint

To cut the spline slot, raise the blade so it protrudes through the slot in the jig cradle. Measure the width across the mitered corner of the workpieces and set the blade height so it cuts one-half to two-thirds of the way across the corner of the miter joint. The spline slot should be centered on the thickness of the joint parts. Cut spline stock from matching or contrasting wood and glue it into the spline slot so the spline grain runs across the joint. Trim the spline flush to the outer edges of the mitered parts

Feather-splined miter joint

Splined miter & bevel joints	
STRESS RESISTANCE:	
Tension: Fair	
Compression: Good	
Shear: Good	
Racking: Good	
COMMON USES:	
Reinforcing miter joints on frames and bevel joints on carcases	

with a hand saw or router and flush-trimming bit.

Cutting splined bevel joints

Cutting splined bevel joints involves first beveling the ends or edges of the joint parts at 45° so the workpieces form a 90° corner when they are assembled. To cut the spline slots, set the beveled edge or end of the workpiece flat on the saw table with the bevel facing down and against the rip fence. Set up the cut so the blade tilts into the workpiece. Adjust the fence until the blade intersects the workpiece near the inside corner of the beveled edge, and raise the blade to 3/8 in. Cut the spline slots with the workpiece held against the miter gauge, sliding the bevel tip along the rip fence. Cut and insert splines just as you would for splined miters or splined butt joints.

Cut spline slots in beveled edges by tilting the blade to 45° and guiding the workpiece through the blade with your miter gauge. Set up the cut by visually aligning the workpiece with the blade: for maximum holding power, the blade should enter the beveled edge very near the inside corner (See *Tip* below). Unplug the saw before setting up for the cut. Because you're not making a through cut, you can use the rip fence to help index the cut.

Proper spline position in miter joints

WEAK

This spline location makes for a weak joint. The areas indicated by the arrows are too narrow, so the outside corner of the miter could break off.

STRONG

The optimal location for the spline is near the inside edge of the joint, leaving a thicker area above the spline.

How to reinforce a frame with feather splines

1 Feather splines provide reinforcement to outside corners on
mitered frames. To cut them safely,
you'll need to build a simple jig like
the one shown on pages 152 to 153.
Once you've built the jig, clamp a
mitered frame into the jig. Set up
the saw so it will cut about one-half
the way through the frame members
when they pass over the blade (See
inset photo). Cut centered spline
slots in all four corners.

2 Cut squares of stock the same
thickness as the spline slots and
glue the squares into the corner
slots. After the glue has set, trim the
feather splines so they're flush with
the edges of the frame. Use a fine-
toothed hand saw to trim the feather
splines. Smooth out the joints
between the splines and the frame
with sandpaper.

Use splines to align and reinforce miter joints

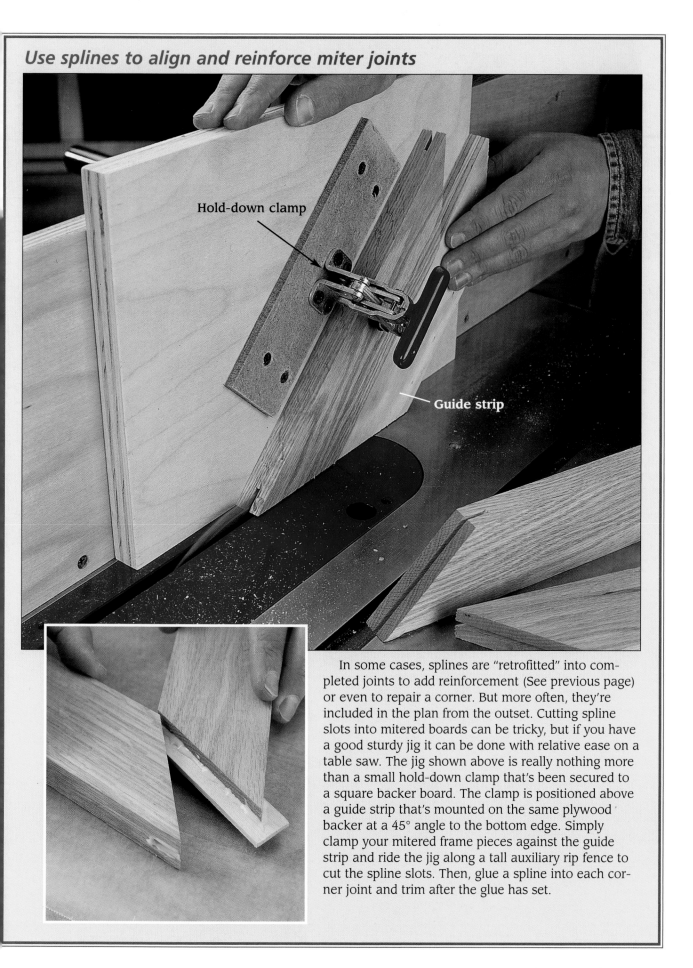

Hold-down clamp

Guide strip

In some cases, splines are "retrofitted" into completed joints to add reinforcement (See previous page) or even to repair a corner. But more often, they're included in the plan from the outset. Cutting spline slots into mitered boards can be tricky, but if you have a good sturdy jig it can be done with relative ease on a table saw. The jig shown above is really nothing more than a small hold-down clamp that's been secured to a square backer board. The clamp is positioned above a guide strip that's mounted on the same plywood backer at a 45° angle to the bottom edge. Simply clamp your mitered frame pieces against the guide strip and ride the jig along a tall auxiliary rip fence to cut the spline slots. Then, glue a spline into each corner joint and trim after the glue has set.

Sawing Accessories

There are plenty of good reasons for modifying a table saw instead of replacing it: Perhaps your machine wasn't exactly top-of-the-line when you bought it. Although the saw may serve 90% of your needs, a couple of features or parts just don't measure up. Maybe the rip fence won't stay parallel to the blade, so it seems like you are adjusting it every time you make a rip cut. Or it could be the saw's miter gauge scale is too crude to set miter cuts accurately. Are the guard and splitter still mounted on your saw? If not, it's probably because these safety devices simply got in the way of your sawing, so you took them off for good. Most saws, regardless of price, suffer from poorly designed guards and splitters. Evaluate those aspects of your saw that suit your needs, then take a hard look at what falls short. A few improved parts may be all you need to perfect the tool you already own.

Accessorizing your saw could be the answer if your woodworking interests demand more from your saw than they once did. Aftermarket accessories could help lift your woodworking skills to a whole new level. If you cut loads of sheet goods, you might consider adding a permanent outfeed support system to your saw to make working with large sheets more manageable. If you find yourself regularly cutting mortise-and-tenon joints, a dedicated tenoning jig makes cutting joint parts a lot faster, easier and more precise. A molding head and cutters might be just the solution you are looking for to create custom profiled molding without investing in a dedicated stationary shaper. In fact, you can even purchase sanding accessories that will convert your table saw into a sanding disk station.

Accessories can make your saw easier to move and cleaner to operate. Maybe you've grown tired of sneezing sawdust every time you spend an afternoon in the shop, and you've decided it's time to buy a dust collection system. You'll need to install a dust port on your saw to connect the saw to the collector. If you own a contractor's or cabinet saw, the chances are good that there's a dust port accessory available to fit it. If floor space is precious in your garage or basement shop, and your saw can't stay in one place at all times, a rolling saw base makes moving your saw less of a chore and much easier on your back.

The following pages offer a sampling of accessories to get you thinking about enhancing the performance and versatility of your saw. You may also find the chart below helpful for evaluating your accessory options. Eventually, you'll probably want to invest in a new saw, and maybe that's the best solution for you now. Only you can be the judge. However, spending a few hundred dollars to make a good saw better could be a more sensible option than investing several times that amount on a brand-new saw.

Accessory options by saw category

ACCESSORY	BENCHTOP SAWS	CONTRACTOR'S SAWS	CABINET SAWS
Fences			
Guards			
Removable splitters			
Mitering attachments			
Workpiece support			
Dado blades/Molding heads			
Sanding accessories			
Dust collection attachments			
Rolling saw bases			

Available for some saws Available for most saws Available for all saws

This T-square fence, built by Delta International Machinery Corporation, has a long aluminum fence body with a massive clamp assembly that attaches to the front rail. Larger clamps provide more support for the fence, which help keep the fence from deflecting during use. The fence body is long enough to suit saw tables of any depth.

Most aftermarket T-square fences resemble this one, built by the Biesemeyer Corporation. These fences can be purchased with a fence rail that spans the length of the saw table only or a longer version for use with a side extension table. Buy a fence that has an easy-to-read measurement scale along the front fence rail.

Rip fences

Until recently, many table saws came equipped with sub-standard rip fences. Rip fences are critical to accurate, clean rip cuts. If the fence on your saw won't stay parallel to the blade, slides roughly and binds along the fence rails even when the rails are clean, or if the fence is difficult to tune, you should consider upgrading your rip fence.

Fence systems have improved considerably of late, but some saws still have lousy fences. Without a reliable and accurate rip fence, you'll never realize your saw's full cutting potential. And you'll constantly fuss with fence adjustments.

If you are happy with your saw, but not your rip fence, take heart. Dozens of manufacturers offer accessory rip fences to fit most popular full-sized saws. When combined with a side extension table, aftermarket rip fences can expand a saw's ripping capacity from around 2 ft. to more than 4 ft. in width (the extension table also provides additional support for crosscutting long workpieces). Unfortunately, the aftermarket saw fence industry still has little to offer benchtop saw owners. This is bound to change as the popularity of benchtop saws continues to grow.

Adding an aftermarket fence will set you back a couple hundred dollars or more, not including the side extension table. The cost of the fence can even exceed what you paid for your saw in the first place. But the difference in performance and reliability will probably more than make up for your initial investment, and you'll wonder how you ever did without a better fence.

Generally, aftermarket rip fences are T-square style, where the fence clamps to a large hollow rail mounted to the front of the saw. The back of the fence rests on either the saw table or a metal ledge that bolts to the back of the saw. Fence bodies are made of extruded aluminum or steel and range in length from 3 to 5 ft to accommodate saw tables of varying depths. Since T-square fences clamp only to the front rail, fence bodies tend to be wider than they are tall to improve lengthwise stiffness.

Some T-square fences are faced on both sides with low-friction melamine plywood or polyethylene plastic to help minimize friction between the workpiece and the fence. Depending on the manufacturer, these laminated or plastic fence faces can be replaced if they are damaged.

On most fences, the clamp assembly that holds the fence to the front rail is massive. Some clamps are outfitted with ball bearings so the fence glides easily along the front rail. Other fence clamps simply slide along the rail.

In terms of retrofitting your saw, the installation process is fairly simple. Aftermarket fences may fit your saw exactly, if it is a popular model. Otherwise, you'll probably need to drill new holes in the saw table to accommodate the bolts that hold the fence system in place.

Incra Precision Tools manufactures a modified T-square style fence with the clamp mechanism located on the side of the saw table rather than the front. The fence slides in channels on rails mounted to the front and back of the saw. In this installation, the white extension wing doubles as a router table.

Features to look for in a rip fence

T-square fence styles are virtually indistinguishable from one another at first glance, but the differences in quality are obvious when you look closely. The best way to choose a rip fence is to examine a few at a woodworking outlet or machinery dealer. Woodworking magazines will review fences occasionally, so read a few articles if testing actual rip fences isn't feasible where you live. When shopping for a new saw fence, here are some features to look for:

• The front clamp should lock solidly and squarely to the front rail. A fence clamp needs to hold the fence in place and stay parallel with the blade. Generally, the broader and more substantial the clamp base, the better.

• Fence movement along the full length of the front rail should be smooth. You should be able to unlock and slide the fence easily from one position to another, regardless of whether the fence rolls on bearings or slides against the rail.

• Every fence will have a measurement scale that stretches along the front rail. Be sure this scale is easy to read. The fence clamp will have some sort of cursor window for indexing the fence off of the blade. It should be prominent and adjustable.

• Adjustment features for squaring the fence to the miter slots and blade

should be easy to operate. Be sure you can square the fence faces with the saw table as well.

• A micro-adjustment knob is a handy accessory, and it comes standard on some fences. This feature allows you to shift the fence in minute increments along the fence rail for precise settings.

The fence body that comes with Delta's Unifence system can be adjusted to any length across the saw table to function like a partial fence (See also page 72).

Adding attachments. Many saw operations will require adding an auxiliary (or *sacrificial*) wood fence to the rip fence. Look for a fence with holes or channels in the fence body that will make this installation easy.

Guard styles

Crank-adjust blade guard. This guard assembly, made by HTC Products, Inc., uses a crank mechanism to raise and lower the acrylic blade shroud over the blade. Two metal posts attach the shroud to the crank housing. By loosening a couple of adjustment knobs, the shroud can be adjusted laterally across the saw table, a useful feature for those instances where the rip fence must be set close to the blade.

Control arm

Delta's Uniguard system features a long control arm that attaches to the back of the saw and to a side extension table. The design creates plenty of clear space for crosscutting to the right of the blade. The control arm is made of two telescoping parts so the guard shroud can be adjusted laterally over the blade. This guard comes with a separate splitter, but not all aftermarket guards do. You may need to create your own splitter.

Guards & splitters

Guards and splitters are your only mechanical lines of defense against injury from a table saw. Guards shield your hands and arms from exposure to the blade, and splitters keep saw kerfs open to help minimize kickback. But when guards and splitters are attached together to form a single piece of saw hardware, they can become clunky to use. They are also easy to knock out of alignment and may even limit your ability to see what's happening close to your cuts. What's worse, some operations, like cutting dadoes, are impossible to do with the splitter in place, so you'll have to remove both the guard and splitter assembly to make the cut.

For any number of reasons, woodworkers commonly remove the blade guard and splitter assembly permanently, despite the risks.

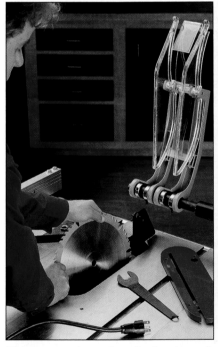

Flip-up convenience. One disadvantage of one-piece guard and splitter assemblies is you'll typically have to remove them for blade changes and maintenance. Delta's Uniguard shroud, on the other hand, conveniently flips up and out of the way for work around the blade.

Important safety features

Aftermarket blade guards operate independently of the splitter, so they can remain in place for making non-through cuts, like dadoes. This setup will shield your hands from the blade, but it still won't protect you from kickback.

Delta's Uniguard shroud splits in two halves, so the shroud can straddle the rip fence, if necessary, to keep the blade covered.

Fortunately, a handful of aftermarket guards are available, and all of them are improvements over the one-piece guard and splitter design. Like aftermarket fences, companies that build replacement guards target the largest segment of the table saw market—full-sized contractor's and cabinet saws. There are no aftermarket blade guards for benchtop saws at this time.

Most aftermarket guards consist of a metal or plastic shroud suspended over the blade from a control arm or a pair of metal rods. The guard floats over the blade so it can work independently of the splitter, which makes cutting with a dado blade much safer. Some aftermarket guards come with a splitter, some don't.

The control arm assemblies on aftermarket guards attach to the saw in several different ways. Some fasten to the back of the saw cabinet with brackets. Others mount to the end of a side extension table on the saw, to the floor or even to the ceiling above the saw. Most control arms have telescoping parts, so the

Removable splitters

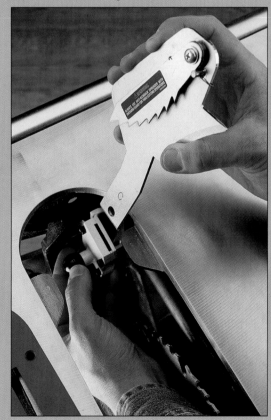

Aftermarket blade guards will protect you from blade exposure, but unless they come with a splitter, you're still vulnerable to kickback. The Biesemeyer Corporation manufactures a removable splitter with antikickback pawls that mounts beneath the throatplate and to the cradle assembly in back of the blade. The splitter installs in a matter of minutes and can be popped in and out in even less time. To remove or replace the splitter, simply lift off the throatplate and pull on a spring-loaded knob at the base of the splitter assembly. The knob connects to a through-pin that holds the splitter in place.

arm can be shortened or lengthened to reposition the guard shroud laterally over the blade. This adjustment feature is important, particularly when a cut requires you to set the rip fence close to the blade. The goal is to keep a guard in place, no matter how close the rip fence gets to the blade. On a standard one-piece guard and splitter, you'd have to remove the guard for rip cuts narrower than about ½ in., in order to squeeze a push-stick in between the rip fence and the blade. Removing the guard is always an unsafe practice.

Blade shrouds must be capable of being raised and lowered to accommodate workpieces of different thicknesses. Some aftermarket guards are counterweighted, so the shroud rides up and over the workpiece, then drops automatically back into place against the saw table when the workpiece leaves the blade. One guard style shown on the previous page requires the operator to raise and lower the shroud with a hand crank each time the workpiece thickness changes. A third guard shroud style splits into two pieces, so each half of the shroud works independently of the other. It's a sensible design because the shroud keeps the blade shielded, no matter how close the rip fence gets to the blade.

Features to consider when buying an aftermarket blade guard & splitter:

• **Lateral adjustment.** Be sure the control arm has a lateral adjustment feature so the shroud can move as the rip fence gets closer to the blade.

• **Crosscutting capacity.** Evaluate how much crosscutting capacity you need to the left and right of the blade. Control arms that mount to the saw or a side extension table will limit your clear space on one side of the blade or the other. If you plan to attach a side extension table to your saw, clear space shouldn't be a problem.

• **Mobility.** If your saw needs to be mobile, you'll want a guard system that mounts directly to the saw, rather than to the floor or ceiling. Buy a guard that disassembles and reassembles easily if your saw gets transported regularly in a vehicle.

• **Splitter.** If the guard system you have in mind does not come with a splitter, be sure your brand of saw will take an aftermarket splitter. Otherwise, you should make your own splitter from a piece of metal or rigid plastic. A guard alone only shields you from exposure to the blade; it won't protect you from kickback.

• **ON/OFF switch.** The control arms of some guards come equipped with an ON/OFF switch to make shutting down the saw possible without reaching underneath the saw table. Although this isn't a necessary feature to have, it is a handy convenience item and gives you an added measure of safety if you should need to shut the saw off in a hurry.

Tenoning jig

If you cut tenons only occasionally, it's probably worth your time to build an inexpensive tenoning jig. Shop-made tenoning jigs are easy to build (See pages 156 to 157), but you've got to construct them carefully. The face of the jig that supports the work must be absolutely square to the saw table, otherwise you won't be able to make the tenon cuts straight, relative to the workpiece.

On the other hand, if you cut tenons for virtually every project you build, a commercial tenoning jig like the one shown here is probably a worthwhile investment. Although relatively pricey, these heavyweight jigs are made of cast iron and steel, so they hold workpieces securely and squarely as you feed them into the blade. A large C-clamp-style screw holds the work against a vertical plate on the jig. The jig base is mounted on a steel bar that fits into and slides along either miter slot.

Tenoning jigs are adjustable in every direction, to suit virtually any tenon-cutting setup. Some even have a tilting feature so you can cut angled tenons as well. One locking lever allows you to tune the jig so the vertical support is precisely square to the table. Another lever controls lateral adjustments for setting up tenon cheek cuts. Better-quality tenon jigs are outfitted with a micro-adjustment knob to dial in precise lateral measurements.

Commercial tenoning jig. If you cut plenty of tenons, you'll appreciate the accuracy and convenience of owning a dedicated tenoning jig. Better-quality models are fully adjustable, sturdy and extremely precise.

Mitering attachments

Cutting accurate miters is the bane of many woodworkers because it's tricky to do accurately. Miter angles that are off by even a degree can throw the joints of a picture frame or edge-banded corner out of whack, leaving an unsightly gap. The trouble is, when you are setting an angle on a standard-issue miter gauge, a two-degree difference is almost imperceptible, especially on low-quality miter gauges. Yet this level of precision is what you'll need to cut dead-on miters. Another problem with making accurate miter cuts is that it is difficult to hold a workpiece steady against the miter gauge fence without the workpiece shifting during the cut.

Several mitering accessories are available to help improve the accuracy of miter cuts. A number of manufacturers offer precision miter gauges with bars that fit the miter slots on most saws. Aftermarket miter gauges feature heftier housings, ultra-precise protractor scales and even auxiliary fence attachments. Some have preset positive holes along the back edge of the protractor housing. A spring-loaded pin snaps into these holes to lock the miter exactly at a number of common angles, including 15°, 22.5°, 30° and 45°.

Another mitering accessory, made by the Dubby Corporation, looks like a modified shooting board (See photo below). The jig is comprised of a melamine-covered sled-style base mounted on a miter slot bar. An adjustable hardwood fence attaches to the top of the jig with lockknobs, and a metal scale runs along the edge of the jig for setting the fence to precise miter angles. The scale is positioned far enough from the

This precision miter gauge features a detailed protractor scale and preset holes for locking the fence at various angles. The gauge also comes with an auxiliary fence for added support.

fence's pivot point that distances between each degree mark are far enough apart to be set exactly. Another benefit to this mitering jig is that the workpiece can't shift during the cut because it is fixed to the jig.

An inexpensive route to improve your existing miter gauge is to fasten on a hold-down clamp. Hold-down miter gauge attachments work like quick-action woodworking clamps. A screw-type mechanism or pistol grip on the miter gauge tightens the workpiece against the miter gauge bar to hold it steady as you cut. The hold-down serves a safety function as well by keeping your hands off the workpiece and clear of the blade.

The Dubby mitering guide is equipped with a melamine covered sled-style base that rides on a bar in the saw's miter slots for maximum workpiece support. A large miter scale, adjustable fence and stopblocks make setting miter cuts easy and precise.

Clamping jigs fasten to your saw's miter gauge and clamp workpieces against the miter gauge bar to hold them securely. Some hold-downs have a knob to tighten the clamp, while others tighten by squeezing a pistol-grip handle.

Molding heads

Trim molding is a common design detail on many woodworking and remodeling projects. You can buy premilled molding in a variety of different profiles made from common wood types like pine and oak, but the cost can be steep. And eventually you'll run into situations where the molding profile you want simply isn't available, or you can't find it in the species of wood you are using in the rest of the project.

Milling your own molding isn't difficult, and you can save money in the long run by milling it yourself on the table saw using a *molding head.* A molding head is a heavy metal hub that spins on the saw arbor like a saw blade. Short steel blades, called *knives,* fit into two to four slots in the molding head. Knives are sold in matching sets, and each set is sharpened along an edge to form one of numerous different molding profiles including beads, coves, flutes and grooves. Several different knife sets will come with the molding head.

Molding heads are somewhat controversial table saw accessories from a safety standpoint. Since you have to attach the knives manually, there's always the chance that you could forget to tighten a knife securely, and it could work loose during a cut and come flying off the cutter head at great speed. Also, since a molding head shapes rather than severs a workpiece, there is no saw kerf, so you can't use a splitter or antikickback

Molding heads **consist of a heavy center hub with two to four slots for holding a set of profiled steel molding knives. Knives are available in a host of different shapes for cutting custom molding. Molding heads should only be used in full-size saws powered by motors of 1½ h.p. or more.**

pawls to safeguard yourself against kickback. The chances for kickback increase the more wood you "hog out" in a single pass.

You can use a molding head safely if you tighten the knives securely when you install them and take precautions to minimize your exposure to the knives when you make cuts. You can buy throatplates for molding heads, but the cutter opening is usually too wide to provide enough support close to the knives. A better alternative is to fabricate a zero-clearance throatplate or clamp a scrap piece of plywood over the throatplate area and raise the molding head through it so that just the cutter profile protrudes through.

In most instances you'll have to bury a portion each knife inside the rip fence. To do this, attach a sacrificial wood fence to the rip fence just as you would when using a dado blade. Set the molding head below the saw table, position the auxiliary wood fence over the knife area and slowly raise the molding head until the knives penetrate the wood fence to the height you need to mill the workpiece.

Cutting molding safely

In addition to using tight-fitting throatplates and wood fences, here are some more tips for using a molding head safely:

• Clamp featherboards beside the workpiece on the infeed side of the molding head to hold workpieces securely against the rip fence. Use a pushing tool to guide the workpiece through the cut.

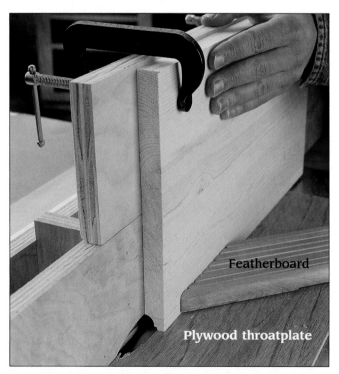

Shape the molding profile on wider pieces of stock **whenever possible, then rip the narrow section of molding from the wider board. Be sure to use a zero-clearance throatplate or a piece of scrap plywood to shield as much of the molding head as possible. Featherboards will hold workpieces tight against the fence.**

• Cut moldings from wider pieces of stock, when possible, to keep your hands a safe distance from the cutters. Then rip the molding to width from the wider stock. For those situations where you must shape narrow stock, clamp a board on top of the workpiece and attach another board to the first to create a narrow "tunnel" over the cutting area (See photo, below). The tunnel will act as both a guard and a hold-down device around the knives. Stand clear of the back tunnel opening in the event a workpiece should shoot back out of the tunnel. When the back end of the workpiece enters the tunnel, use a long scrap piece of the same dimensions to push the workpiece through and finish the cut.

• Double-check that the knives are tight in the molding head before installing it on the saw and beginning a cutting operation.

• Regardless of the profile you are cutting, make a series of shallow passes, increasing the depth of cut by no more than 1⁄16 in. at a time.

Cutting narrow molding safely

Molding "tunnel." In cases where you must cut molding on narrow workpieces, create a "tunnel" from scrapwood to support and guide workpieces as you feed them over the knives. Pushsticks alone will not give you the holding power you'll need to control your work. Use a scrap pushstick of the same dimensions as your workpieces to push the wood strips through the tunnel.

The molding "tunnel" consists of a sacrificial rip fence (A), a top support (B), side support (C) and either a zero-clearance throatplate or a piece of scrap plywood (D). The tunnel holds a workpiece (E) in place over the knives.

Sanding disks

Convert your table saw into a sanding station by installing an aftermarket sanding accessory. The typical sanding kit includes a 10-in. metal plate and one or more circular sandpaper disks with adhesive backing. The plate mounts to the saw arbor just like a saw blade and fits through the throatplate opening. Depending on the manufacturer, some metal plates are flat on one face and tapered on the other. The tapered side makes it easy to sand chamfers, especially when you tilt the sanding plate. Sandpaper disks come in a variety of coarsenesses, from 60- to 180-grit, to suit most sanding tasks. NOTE: *If you plan to do a lot of heavy disk sanding, buy a dedicated sanding station rather than using your table saw. Saw arbors are not engineered to withstand the kind of continual lateral stresses associated with sanding disks.*

Workpiece support

Any time you are making rip-cuts or crosscuts on workpieces that project more than a few feet beyond the saw table, you'll need a support device alongside or in back of the saw to keep workpieces from tipping off the saw. You could set up one or more roller stands or slide a work table near the saw to support your work (See page 64), and these are fine solutions for occasional oversized cuts. However, if your woodworking involves frequent work with full-sized sheets of plywood or long lengths of stock, consider adding a dedicated extension table, outfeed roller platform or sliding table to your saw instead.

Laminate-covered side extension tables are fairly common features on new saws that come with T-square rip fences, but you can mount an extension table to any saw. Typically, the extension table attaches to a steel base and replaces one of the saw's extension wings. The rip fence rails then attach to both the saw and the extension table. Some manufacturers offer laminated outfeed tables as well, for even more support. Another option for outfeed support is to bolt a roller platform to the back of the saw. These platforms are fashioned from a dozen or more ball-bearing tubular rollers (similar to those found on roller stands) into a metal frame. The platform is mounted on hinges so it can be tipped up and into position when needed or folded down flat against the saw to conserve floor space.

If your woodworking could benefit from a side extension table and your saw could benefit from better mitering control as well, consider adding a sliding table attachment. Sliding tables consist of a movable extension wing mounted to a metal frame that rides on ball bearings against the right- or left-hand side of the saw. A long fence attached to the table provides plenty of support behind your work and probably will come with a *flip stop* or two for making repetitive crosscuts. The fences on most sliding tables can be pivoted along a protractor scale for setting precise miter cuts.

Sliding table

Pivoting fence

Sliding tables **mount to the side of the saw, replacing one of the saw's extension wings. The one shown here is made by Delta. Sliding tables offer superior workpiece support for crosscutting, because the whole table glides past the blade. This way, the workpiece can't shift during a cut. A long fence on the back of the saw table may even pivot on some models.**

This outfeed roller table, **made by HTC Products, Inc., is large enough to make other outfeed devices unnecessary, yet it folds down flat against the saw when not in use to conserve space.**

Dust collection attachments

You don't have to cut much wood in an enclosed space to realize how beneficial it is to connect the saw to a dust collection system. Table saws generate the lion's share of shop sawdust and chips, and quantities of this debris build up in hurry. If cleaner air isn't enough of an incentive, connecting your saw to a dust collector also makes shop cleanup a snap. The majority of saw waste will get sucked into a disposable bag on the collector. When the bag fills, just wind up the top and throw it away.

Many cabinet saws come with a 4- or 5-in. round dust collection port built right into the saw base. It's sized to fit directly inside a flexible dust collection hose that attaches to the dust collector. Cabinet saws that don't come with a port will have some sort of removable panel or hole in the cabinet for installing a dust collection attachment with a hose port. These port attachments are inexpensive and available from the saw manufacturer. Or you can fabricate your own with a section of 4-in.-dia. stovepipe or ductwork and a piece of sheet metal.

It's more difficult to corral all the dust and chips produced from a contractor's saw because both the bottom and the back of the saw base are open. Some manufacturers sell a tray with a round dust port built in that fits over the bottom of the saw base. If a similar attachment isn't available for your saw, cover the bottom of the saw base with a piece of ¼-in. plywood fitted with a hose port. You may also want to consider covering the back of your contractor's saw with plywood to cut down on dust. A back plate will also improve the suction through the bottom plate hose port. Make cutouts for the drive belt and splitter/guard assembly. Be aware that this back plate will need to be removed when you tilt the saw arbor, since the entire motor assembly will tilt with the arbor and hit the back plate.

Most new benchtop saws have a port for attaching dust collection, but older saws may not. If your saw doesn't, you may want to consider designing a saw station with a dust collection chamber and port built in. Since the bottom of the saw base on benchtop saws is open, build a box-type saw stand beneath the saw to capture falling sawdust.

Regardless of which saw you own and how you attach your dust collection system to the tool, saw with a guard in place. A saw guard not only shields you from the blade, it also helps to direct dust and chips back down into the saw base rather than into the air.

Screw-on dust collection attachment. Cabinet saws that don't come with a round dust port connection can be retrofitted with attachments to make dust collection possible. This saw has an opening in the cabinet for a screw-on dust collection attachment available from the manufacturer.

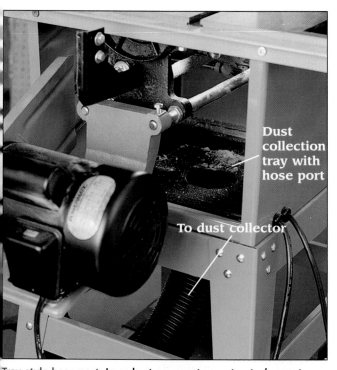

Dust collection tray with hose port

To dust collector

Tray-style hose port. In order to connect a contractor's saw to a dust collector, you'll have to install a tray with a hose port to cover the bottom of the saw base. Some manufacturers offer these trays as aftermarket accessories for the saw. Or you can build your own from a piece of plywood outfitted with a plastic or sheet-metal hose port.

Rolling saw bases

Who doesn't want to have a dedicated shop space with enough room for each and every stationary tool? If you are not yet woodworking in your dream shop, it's likely you need to move tools around in order to use them, then move them out of the way to make room for other things that share your shop space, like cars or recreational equipment. A table saw is probably the first tool you'll get tired of dragging across the floor. The job gets much easier when you put your saw on wheels.

A number of manufacturers offer rolling bases custom-sized to fit full-sized saws. Extension tables are becoming so popular on saws these days that you can even buy one-piece roller stands custom fitted to fit the extension table.

Roller stands commonly consist of a steel frame outfitted with a number of wheels that fits underneath the saw base. One or more of the wheels typically lock into position with a foot-operated lever. When the wheels flip up, the saw drops down to the floor and is ready for use. Lower the wheels, and the base lifts up off the floor to roll the saw away.

If you'd rather not buy a prefabricated rolling base, you can buy kits with brackets and wheels to build a

One-piece steel rolling saw bases are available to fit virtually any brand of saw. You can even purchase bases that accommodate side extension tables, like the one mounted on this cabinet saw. Rolling bases turn an otherwise stationary tool into one that can be moved easily by one person.

base that will fit any saw or stationary tool. To use these bases, you'll cut lengths of hardwood to span the distance between the corner brackets and essentially build the framework yourself.

Portable saw base. Outfit your benchtop saw with a portable saw base, like Delta's Sidekick saw stand, and you'll truly have a table saw that can go anywhere, indoors or out.

Saw base kit. A low-cost alternative to custom saw bases is to buy a rolling saw base kit and build it yourself. The kit comes with four metal corner brackets, wheels and the foot pedal assembly that raises and lowers the saw. You supply hardwood struts to connect the brackets.

Converting a saw motor from 115 to 230 volts

If your table saw is a contractor's or cabinet style, it is likely powered by an induction motor. Induction motors run at slower speeds and provide more constant horsepower under load than their lighter-weight counterparts, called universal motors. Induction motors are built for heavy, constant use. Universal motors are lighter-duty power plants usually found in portable tools like drills and circular saws, as well as most benchtop table saws.

One advantage to having an induction motor in your saw is that many manufacturers give you the option of rewiring the motor to run off 230-volt current rather than 115-volt household current. What this means for your saw is that it will run at half the amperage required when the motor is wired for 115 volts. Lower amperage means lower heat buildup—not more power. Over the long haul, less heat generated by the motor results in longer motor life. And the higher voltage supplied to the motor means it is less vulnerable to the significant voltage drops that occur when you plug your 115-volt saw into long extension cords.

It's easy to tell whether you can rewire the motor on your saw from one voltage to another. Motors that can be rewired will give you a wiring schematic right on the motor housing. Or, you may be able to find this information by removing the plate that covers the box where the power cord enters the motor. Your owner's manual should make this information clear as well.

Making the switch

It really isn't difficult to convert your saw from 115- to 230-volt power, but of course your shop will need 230-volt service in order to plug the saw in. These higher voltage outlets actually have two "hot" wire leads rather than just one, and each of these hot wires supplies half the voltage the motor requires—or 115 volts each. A third wire in the 230-volt scheme serves as both a ground and a neutral lead. You can distinguish a 230-volt outlet from a 115; the top two slots for the plug prongs are oriented horizontally rather than vertically, so they look quite different from the typical three-prong household outlet. This configuration keeps you from unknowingly plugging a 115-volt appliance into a 230-volt outlet.

When you rewire an induction motor, what you'll effectively do is turn the power cord's white, "neutral" wire into a "hot" wire, which connects to a second unused hot wire inside the motor. The changeover is perfectly safe as long as you follow the instructions printed on the schematic drawing. A second change you'll need to make is to remove the 115-volt plug at the end of the motor power cord and replace it with a 230-volt plug. The power cord on motors designed for two voltages will be made of a wire gauge heavy enough to carry either 115- or 230-volt current safely. If you'd rather not splice on a new plug, you could replace the power cord altogether with one fitted with a 230-volt plug. Check with the manufacturer of your saw or buy the cord from an electric motor supplier in your area.

Induction motors that can be converted from 115 to 230 volts have a wiring schematic printed on the motor housing or on a removable cover to show you how to connect the wires. Follow the diagram carefully.

Making the conversion to higher voltage will require you to either splice on a new plug or replace the entire power cord. Notice that 230-volt plugs have two prongs that are turned 90° from a standard three-prong grounded plug.

1. Crosscut Sled

5/16" wide × 3/8" deep dadoes, spaced 3 in. apart

Slot for saw blade

#8 × 1 5/8" flathead wood screws

3/4" brads

#8 × 1 1/4" flathead wood screws

Crosscut sleds slide across the saw table from front to back and support workpieces that are too large to be guided effectively with the miter gauge. They are also helpful for making rip cuts and crosscuts on pieces that are too small to be held safely with a pushstick. For more on crosscut sleds, see page 85.

The sled you see here has a pair of hardwood rails that ride in the miter slots on the saw table. The rails are fastened to a plywood base the same size as the saw table. The rails keep the sled traveling parallel to the blade as you push it across the saw. The base actually splits into two parts to make room for a blade slot, and plywood fences on the front and back of the jig hold the base parts in position. The fence on the infeed side of the saw also serves as a right-angle guide to support workpieces from behind, like a miter gauge.

For safety, an acrylic blade guard slides up and down in dado slots on both fences to protect you from blade exposure. A plywood blade tunnel mounted to the back of the sled keeps the blade shielded in cases where the blade must pass through the infeed fence.

Crosscut Sled Cutting List

Part	No.	Size	Material
A. Base	1	3/4 × 27 1/2 × 36 in.*	Plywood
B. Fence	4	3/4 × 24 × 6 in.	"
C. Tunnel (side)	2	3/4 × 3 × 5 in.	"
D. Tunnel (top)	1	3/4 × 3 × 5 in.	"
E. Mounting plate	1	1/4 × 4 3/4 × 5 in.	"
F. Miter slot rail	2	3/8 × 23/32 × 27 1/2 in.*	Hardwood
G. Guard (end)	2	3/4 × 4 × 3 in.	Plywood
H. Guard (side)	2	1/4 × 4 × 24 1/8 in.	Acrylic
I. Guard (top)	1	1/4 × 3 1/2 × 23 3/8 in.	"

* Adjust part dimensions to fit your saw

Crosscut sleds ensure that you'll make accurate, square cuts on workpieces that are too wide or long to be supported effectively by the miter gauge.

How to build a crosscut sled

PHOTO A: Draw marks across the edges of the base and the ends of the rails on both the infeed and outfeed side of the saw table to reference the alignment of these parts. Line up these marks when you fasten the rails to the sled base.

3 in.

PHOTO B: Cut pairs of ⁵⁄₁₆-in.-wide, ³⁄₈-in.-deep dadoes on each fence to serve as tracks for the blade guard. Space the slots 3 in. apart and center them on each fence.

1 Cut the base and miter slot rails to size, according to the *Cutting List,* previous page. Size the base to match the dimensions of your saw table and the rails to match the width and depth of the miter slots. The rails should fit snugly in the miter slots and slide back and forth without binding.

2 Place the rails in the miter slots, then set the sled base on the saw table. Position the base so the ends and edges are flush with the saw table all around. Draw marks across the edges of the base and the ends of the rails on both the infeed and outfeed side of the saw table to reference the alignment of these parts **(See Photo A)**.

3 Remove the sled base and rails from the saw and attach the rails to the base. Spread wood glue on the edges of the rails that face the sled base, align the rails with the alignment marks you drew on the base in Step 2, and fasten the rails to the base with ¾-in. brads. NOTE: *Attach one rail first, then set the sled on the saw table with the other rail in the miter slot. Check to make sure your alignment marks haven't changed for attaching the second rail as a result of attaching the first rail.* It's crucial that the rails align perfectly with the miter slots once you've attached the rails to the base, or the sled won't fit properly into both miter slots at the same time.

4 Cut the four fence pieces to size. Fasten pairs of fence pieces together with glue and 1¼-in. wood screws to form two thick fences. We shaped the fences to be taller in the center in order to accommodate dado slots for the sliding blade guard but shorter on the ends to make it easier to hold workpieces against the fences. The fences are 3 in. tall on the ends and increase to 6 in. tall in the guard area. We made the guard area on each fence 8 in. long.

5 Cut pairs of 5⁄16-in.-wide, 3⁄8-in.-deep dadoes on one face of each fence to serve as tracks for the blade guard. Space the slots 3 in. apart and center them on each fence. Use a dado blade in the table saw to cut the slots **(See Photo B).**

6 Center one fence on one end of the jig base, perpendicular to the miter slot rails. Fasten the fence in place by driving 15⁄8-in. screws through the base from beneath and into the fence. Set the jig on the saw, raise the blade so it cuts through the base, and cut a saw kerf through the fence and across the entire base **(See Photo C).**

7 Attach the second fence, using a carpenter's square to make sure it's perpendicular to the saw kerf **(See Photo D).** Center the fence on the saw kerf and position the outside face of this fence 3⁄4 in. in from the edge of the sled base to serve as a lip for supporting the blade tunnel. Fasten the fence to the base with screws. Work carefully; it is critical that this fence be exactly square to the saw kerf, as it will serve as a right-angle miter-style guide for the sled.

8 Build the blade tunnel by cutting the sides and top piece to size and attaching them with screws. Fasten the tunnel to the mounting plate with screws, then attach the mounting plate to the outside face of the fence you attached in Step 7.

9 Build the blade guard. Cut the two plywood guard end pieces to size. Cut the 1⁄4-in.-thick acrylic guard sides and top using a fine-toothed plywood blade on the table saw. Sand the cut edges with emery paper. Drill countersunk pilot holes through the guard top and side pieces and into the guard ends. NOTE: *The guard ends should be flush with the ends of the top piece. The guard sides are longer and should overhang the top on either end to form runners that will fit in the fence dadoes.* Assemble the guard with 11⁄4-in. wood screws **(See Photo E).**

PHOTO C: Attach the outfeed-side fence to the sled base with screws. Raise the blade so it will cut through the base, and cut the blade slot across the base.

PHOTO D: Fasten the second fence to the sled, using a carpenter's square to make sure it's perpendicular to the saw kerf.

Guard sides

Guard top

PHOTO E: Drive countersunk wood screws through the acrylic top and side guard pieces to attach them to the guard ends. The guard sides will extend past the guard ends to serve as runners for the guard to slide in the fence dadoes.

2. Tall Auxiliary Fence

Tall fences provide extra support whenever you need to cut a wide or long board with the workpiece standing on edge or end against the rip fence. You could bolt a wide piece of scrap directly to your metal rip fence, but fastening it this way is inconvenient if you need to take the fence on and off frequently. Build this tall fence jig instead, and you'll be able to clamp and unclamp the jig to the rip fence to install or remove it.

Keep the area of the fence next to the saw blade free of screws.

**#8 × 1⅝"
flathead wood
screws, typ.**

Tall Fence Cutting List			
Part	**No.**	**Size**	**Material**
A. Fence	1	¾ × 36 × 10 in.*	Plywood
B. Clamp rail	1	¾ × 3 × 36 in.*	"
C. Base	1	¾ × 2½ × 36 in.*	"
D. Braces	3	¾ × 2½ × 9 in.	"
* Adjust part lengths to fit your saw			

Attach a tall auxiliary fence to your rip fence whenever you need to cut a wide or long workpiece on edge or on end against the rip fence. The tall fence provides more vertical bearing support for the workpiece. This fence design clamps quickly and easily to the rip fence.

How to build a tall auxiliary fence

1 Cut the fence and base parts to size. We used cabinet-grade plywood for the entire fence, but you could also use other dimensionally stable materials like medium-density fiberboard (MDF) or particleboard to ensure that the fence parts will stay flat. Whatever sheet stock you choose to use, make sure the side of the fence that faces the blade is smooth. It will serve as the bearing surface for your workpieces, which need to slide smoothly past the blade when you cut them.

2 Fasten the fence to the base with 1⅝-in. flathead wood screws **(See Photo A).** Lay out locations for the screws keeping them clear of the blade area. Drill countersunk pilot holes for the screws first so the screw heads will sit flush with or slightly below the fence face.

3 Cut the three braces to size. Be sure the bottom corners of the braces are square—they are responsible for keeping the tall fence square to the saw table. The braces will sit on top of the base and between the back face of the fence and the clamp rail. Attach the fence to the braces with screws. Position the center brace screws higher on the fence than the maximum blade height for your saw.

4 Rip and crosscut the clamp rail, and attach it to the fence base and braces with screws **(See Photo B).** The bottom edge of the clamp rail should be flush with the bottom of the fence base.

5 Ease sharp edges of the fence with sandpaper. To add durability and to create a slippery smooth bearing surface, cover the fence face with plastic laminate. You could also apply a few coats of gloss polyurethane varnish.

PHOTO A: Fasten the fence to the base with 1⅝-in. wood screws. Keep screws clear of the area on the fence where the blade will be when the fence is on the saw table.

PHOTO B: Attach the clamp rail with screws to the back square edges of the braces. Fasten the clamp rail to the fence base as well.

3. Adjustable Tapering Jig

This adjustable tapering jig will allow you to cut accurate tapers with minimal set-up time. Tapers reduce the proportions of workpieces like chair and table legs by cutting them lengthwise and at an angle to the blade.

Adjustable tapering jigs, like the design shown here, can be set and locked at a range of different angles to suit different taper dimensions. One leg of the jig rides against the rip fence. The other leg, outfitted with a short stopblock, supports the workpiece. For information on using a tapering jig, see pages 76 to 78.

¾" × 1" butt hinge

#10 × ¾" panhead wood screw

Lid support

1¼" washer & wing nut

A

A

A

C

¼" × 1¼" flathead machine screw

B

½" × ½" dado

¾" dia.

Tapering Jig Cutting List			
Part	**No.**	**Size**	**Material**
A. Arm	2	4/4 × 2½ × 22⅜ in.	Hardwood
B. Stopblock	1	½ × 1 × 1 in.	"
C. Handle	1	¾ × 4½ in.	Dowel

Additional hardware required:

(2) ¾ × 1-in. butt hinge with screws

(1) 6-in. metal lid support

(1) ¼ × 1¼-in. flathead machine screw, washer, wing nut

Tapering jigs allow you to cut a workpiece lengthwise and at an angle to the blade to trim tapers. This tapering jig project uses metal lid support hardware to lock the arms at a range of different taper angles.

How to build a tapering jig

1 Rip and crosscut the two jig legs to size from flat, straight hardwood.

2 Cut a ½ × ½-in. dado into the edge of one leg, 1 in. from one end, to house the stopblock **(See Photo A).** Cut the stopblock to size and glue it into the dado. NOTE: *Glue alone is sufficient to hold the stopblock in place. Do not fasten the block in place with a screw. This way, if the blade should ever come into contact with the stopblock, the blade will not hit a fastener.*

3 Cut the dowel handle to length from ¾-in. dowel, and install the dowel handle into the leg that will ride against the saw fence. Drill a ¾-in.-dia. guide hole through the leg, about 1 in. from one end and one edge. Glue the dowel in place.

4 Fasten the legs together with a ¾ × 1-in. butt hinge, attaching the hinge leaves to the ends of the legs opposite the stopblock and handle.

5 Install the metal lid support. NOTE: *Depending on the hardware you buy, you may have to first remove a short angle bracket attached to some lid support hardware. The bracket will not work on this tapering jig. To remove the bracket, drill through or grind off the rivet that fastens the bracket to the curved lid support brace.* Attach the lid support to the top face of the "stopblock" leg with a panhead screw. Place the screw 13⅜ in. from the hinge end of the jig and ½ in. from the inside edge of the leg. Drill a countersunk guide hole into the "handle" leg up from beneath the leg, 12¼ in. from the hinge end and ¾ in. from the inside edge. Insert the machine screw into the guide hole and through the slit in the lid support. Secure the machine screw to the lid support with a washer and wing nut **(See Photo B).**

PHOTO A: Cut a ½ × ½-in. dado into the edge of one leg, 1 in. from one end, to house the stopblock. The stopblock will be attached to the jig arm with glue only, so the dado provides more support.

PHOTO B: Attach the metal lid support to the jig arms, using the screw location information outlined in Step 5.

4. Spline-cutting Jig

Spline-cutting jigs allow you to cut slots across the corners of miter and bevel joints in order to insert thin wooden splines. Splines strengthen and add a decorative element to a variety of wood joints, including picture frame, butt and box joints.

Some spline cuts will require you to hold mating boards at a 45° angle off the saw table. For those kinds of cuts, the spline-cutting jig shown here employs a deep "V"-shaped cradle to support both boards and a back stop for clamping the workpieces securely while you saw. The cradle rests on a tunnel-type blade guard. The entire jig rides on a sled-style base and is guided across the blade by sliding the jig against the rip fence. For a demonstration on how to cut spline joints with this jig, see page 128.

#8 × 1¼"
flathead
wood
screws, typ.

Saw kerf

Spline-cutting Jig Cutting List

Part	No.	Size	Material
A. Base	1	¾ × 10 × 18 in.	Plywood
B. Tunnel (sides)	2	¾ × 4 × 11 in.	"
C. Tunnel (top)	1	¾ × 7 × 7 in.	"
D. Handle	1	¾ × 3 × 4¾ in.	"
E. Cradle	2	¾ × 10 × 10 in.	"
F. Back stop	1	¾ × 9⅞ × 9⅞ in.	"
G. Braces	2	¾ × 4 × 4 in.	"

Some spline cuts will require you to hold workpieces at a 45° angle off the saw table, such as when making "feather" spline joints for picture frames (See inset photo, right). This spline-cutting jig provides a large 90° cradle for clamping workpieces in position. The jig rides along the rip fence, so the blade passes through the jig base and cradle to cut a spline slot in the workpieces.

How to build a spline-cutting jig

1 Rip- and cross-cut the plywood base and three tunnel parts to size. Miter-cut one end of both tunnel sides to 45°. Bevel-cut one edge of the tunnel top to 45°.

2 Attach the tunnel sides to the top of the base with 1¼-in. flathead wood screws. Position one tunnel side so it is flush with a base corner and aligned with the long edge of the base. The mitered edge of the tunnel side piece should face up. Fasten the second tunnel side to the base so the outside faces of the tunnel sides are 7 in. apart and the ends of the tunnel parts align. Fasten the tunnel top to the sides with the bevel edge facing up **(See Photo A).**

3 Rip-cut and cross-cut the back stop and two cradle pieces to size. Cut the square back stop in half, diagonally, to form two triangles (you'll only need one triangle to serve as the back stop). Bevel-cut one end of each cradle piece to 45°. Set the back stop between the cradle pieces, and arrange the beveled ends of the cradle to form a short, flat surface at the bottom of the cradle assembly. Center the back stop along the width of the cradle. Attach the cradle pieces to the back stop with screws **(See Photo B).**

4 Set the cradle assembly in place on the jig base, resting the back of the cradle against the blade tunnel. Align the edges of the cradle with the edges of the base. Drive countersunk 1¼-in screws through the cradle and into the blade tunnel sides.

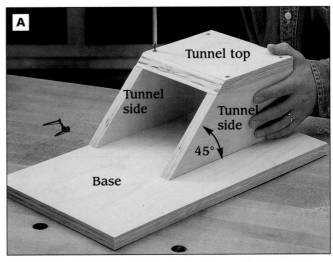

PHOTO A: Attach the tunnel sides to the base with 1¼-in. flathead wood screws. Position one tunnel side so it is flush with a base corner and aligned with the long edge of the base. Fasten the tunnel top to the sides with the bevel edge facing up.

5 Cut a 4 × 4-in. plywood square in half diagonally to form the two triangular braces. Attach the braces to the back face of the cradle, opposite the blade tunnel. Attach the braces to the jig base as well **(See Photo C).**

6 Cut and fasten the handle to the jig base next to the blade tunnel.

NOTE: *When you use the jig for the first time, set the jig in place against the rip fence. Measure the distance from the slot location you'll cut on your workpiece to the rip fence, and use this as the index for cutting a saw kerf across the jig base and cradle.*

PHOTO B: Set the back stop between the cradle pieces. Arrange the beveled ends of the cradle to form a short, flat surface at the bottom of the cradle assembly. Attach the parts with screws.

PHOTO C: Drive countersunk wood screws through the cradle and into the tunnel sides to attach the cradle to the tunnel sides. Then attach the braces to the cradle and base with screws.

5. *Outfeed Table*

Outfeed tables are a more stable alternative to roller stands for supporting long boards when you cut them on the table saw. The problem with most outfeed tables is they don't fold up or come apart for easy storage, so they take up valuable shop floor space.

If you have a small shop where space is at a premium, you'll appreciate the outfeed table shown here. The jig base mounts in the vise of a portable workbench or can be clamped to a sawhorse. The base is not permanently attached between the support pieces, so the tabletop and base slide apart for easy storage. Plus, since the jig clamps into a workbench or to a sawhorse, you can adjust the outfeed table height to suit any saw by raising or lowering the jig base in the clamps.

A

B

C

C

B

D

**#8 × 1⁵⁄₈"
flathead
wood
screws, typ.**

Outfeed Table Cutting List

Part	No.	Size	Material
A. Tabletop	1	¾ × 18 × 36 in.	Plywood
B. Support	2	¾ × 12 × 6 in.	"
C. Side	2	¾ × 6 × 18 in.	"
D. Base	1	¾ × 18 × 18 in.	"

Outfeed tables provide extra support behind or alongside the saw when cutting long or wide boards. This outfeed table can be clamped to a portable workbench or even to a sawhorse. The whole table can be adjusted up or down to match the table height of any saw.

How to build an outfeed table

1 Rip and crosscut the plywood sides and supports to size. The supports are 12 in. wide at the top but slope to 2¼ in. wide at the bottom. Make the angled cuts on the supports with a power miter saw, jig saw or band saw.

2 Fasten the supports to the sides with 1⅝-in. wood screws. Slip ¾-in.-thick scrap spacers between the sides when you attach the parts to create a ¾-in.-wide slot for the base **(See Photo A).** Drive screws through the supports and into the ends of the sides. Remove the spacers to complete the subassembly.

3 Cut the tabletop and base to size. Center the subassembly you built in Step 2 on the tabletop and trace its profile to serve as a drilling guide. Lay out positions for screws in the outline area, keeping screws clear of the recess between the sides. Drill countersunk pilot holes through the tabletop. Line up the subassembly beneath the tabletop and attach it to the tabletop with wood screws **(See Photo B).**

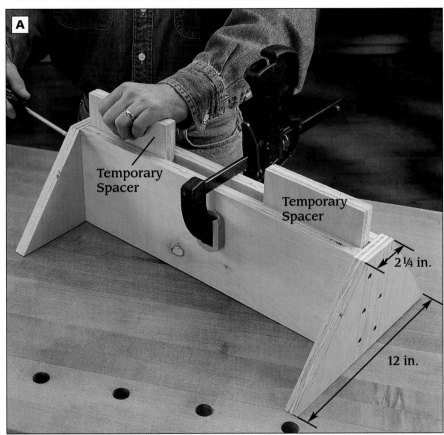

Temporary Spacer

Temporary Spacer

2¼ in.

12 in.

PHOTO A: Attach the supports to the sides. Insert ¾-in.-thick spacers between the sides to allow room for the base later.

PHOTO B: Drive countersunk 1⅝-in. wood screws down through the tabletop and into the supports and sides.

6. Tenoning Jig

¼" × ¾"
dado

D

#8 × 1¼"
**flathead
wood screws**

B

E

C

3¼"

C

A

#8 × 1⅝"
**flathead
wood screws**

¼" × ¾"
rabbet

When you need to cut tenons with a workpiece standing on-end on the saw table, a tenoning jig will provide the vertical support you'll need to make these cuts safely. A tenoning jig acts like a movable tall fence with a back stop attached to support workpieces from behind.

Tenoning jigs have other uses as well, including cutting through-mortises, rabbets or dadoes in the ends of boards.

This tenoning jig is a snap to use. Simply clamp the workpiece against the tall support and the back stop so the end of the workpiece touches the saw table. Set the edge of the jig base (the edge closest to the handle) against the rip fence. Adjust the position of the rip fence and jig until the saw blade lines up with the cutting lines on the workpiece. To make your cuts, slide the jig along the rip fence and past the blade.

Tenoning Jig Cutting List

Part	No.	Size	Material
A. Base	1	¾ × 6 × 8 in.	Plywood
B. Tall support	1	¾ × 8 × 8 in.	"
C. Brace	2	¾ × 2¾ × 2¾ in.	"
D. Handle	1	¾ × 3 × 4¾ in.	"
E. Back stop	1	¾ × 8 × 1½ in.	"

Tenoning jigs support tall, narrow workpieces on-end for cutting tenons, rabbets or through-mortises. To use the jig, clamp a board against the back stop so the end of the board rests against the saw table. Set the jig against the rip fence, and adjust the rip fence and jig until the blade aligns with the layout marks on your workpiece. Slide the jig along the rip fence to make the cut.

How to build a tenoning jig

1 Rip and crosscut the tall support to size. Cut a ¼-in.-deep, ¾-in.-wide rabbet into one of the faces of the support along one long edge. This rabbet will house the edge of the jig base.

2 Cut a ¼-in.-deep, ¾-in.-wide dado into the opposite face of the tall support, ½ in. in from the end **(See Photo A).** This dado should run perpendicular to the rabbet you cut in Step 1. The back stop will fit into this dado. Since not all ¾-in. plywood is exactly ¾-in. thick, check the stock you plan to use for the back stop, and adjust the dado width as needed so the back stop will fit snugly.

3 Cut the base piece. Glue and clamp the tall support to the base. Check the fit of the parts to ensure that they are perpendicular.

4 Cut a 2¾-in.-square of plywood in half diagonally to form the two braces. Fasten the braces to the back of the tall support and top of the base with 1¼-in. wood screws **(See Photo B).**

5 Drive countersunk screws through the tall support and into the back stop to fasten the parts **(See Photo C).** Position these screws at least 3¼ in. up from the jig base to keep them out of reach of the saw blade.

6 Cut and screw the handle to the base next to the braces.

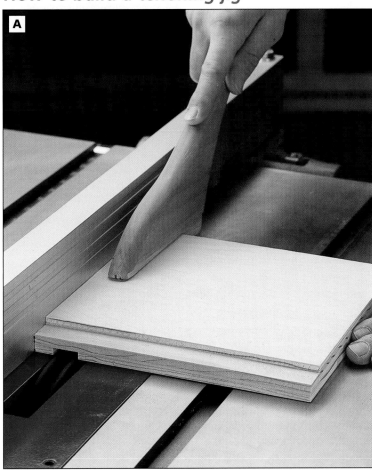

PHOTO A: Cut a ¼-in.-deep, ¾-in.-wide rabbet into one of the faces of the support along one long edge. This rabbet will house the edge of the jig base. Then cut a ¼-in.-deep, ¾-in.-wide dado into the opposite face of the tall support, ½ in. in from the end to fit the back stop.

PHOTO B: Attach the braces to the tall support and jig base with 1¼-in. wood screws.

PHOTO C: Cut the back stop to size and fasten it to the tall support with screws.

Index